EAT WELL, STAY SLIM

Your favourite recipes made healthy

Health&Fitness
MAGAZINE

Words Siân Lewis
Recipes Lyndon Gee
Photography Gareth Sambidge

Editor Mary Comber
Chief sub-editor Eve Boggenpoel
Sub-editors Sharon Gray, Charlie Jackson
Art editor Lucy Pinto
Designer Cara Furman

MagBook Publisher Dharmesh Mistry
Digital Production Manager Nicky Baker
Operations Director Robin Ryan
MagBook Account Manager Katie Wood
MagBook Account Executive Simone Daws
Managing Director of Advertising Julian Lloyd-Evans
Newstrade Director David Barker
Retail & Commercial Director Martin Belson
Publisher Nicola Bates
Group Publisher Russell Blackman
Group Managing Director Ian Westwood
Chief Operating Officer Brett Reynolds
Group Finance Director Ian Leggett
Chief Executive James Tye
Chairman Felix Dennis

MAG**BOOK**

The MagBook brand is a trademark of Dennis Publishing Ltd. 30 Cleveland St, London W1T 4JD. Company registered in England. All material © Dennis Publishing Ltd, licensed by Felden 2013, and may not be reproduced in whole or part without the consent of the publishers.

Eat Well, Stay Slim ISBN1-78106-161-0
To license this product please contact Carlotta Serantoni on +44 (0) 20 79076550 or email carlotta_serantoni@dennis.co.uk
To syndicate content from this product please contact Anj Dosaj Halai on +44(0) 20 7907 6132
or email anj_dosaj-halai@dennis. co.uk

The health and diet information presented in this book is an educational resource
and is not intended as a substitute for medical advice.

We are #TheEverydayActive

ZICO: Regain your balance. Renew your day.

ZICO is rich in potassium, the essential electrolyte that helps maintain normal muscle function, and low in calories. With zero fat and no added sugar* it's the ideal way to refresh your day. Now in a re-sealable bottle, ZICO can always be on hand so you can enjoy the benefits of coconut water throughout the day.

Find ZICO in Waitrose and selected Tesco and Sainsbury's stores and independent retailers. For more details visit zico.com/uk

*Only naturally occurring sugar from the coconuts

 ZICOUK   ZICO_LONDON   ZICOGB

ZICO®
COCONUT WATER

Contents

p22

Contents

p41

IN THE KITCHEN

THE RECIPES

p34

p67

p36

FINAL THOUGHTS

Spring all year round...

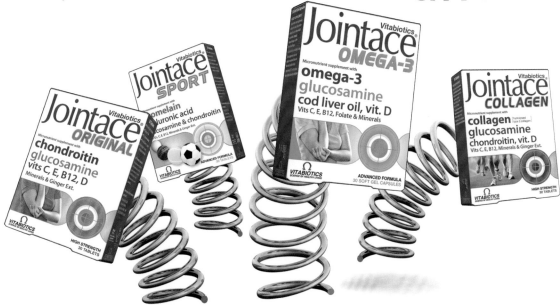

Cartilage and bone health are important for long term wellbeing and an active life. If you are looking for a daily supplement to give you extra support from within, *Jointace®* range has been specially formulated by Vitabiotics' experts to provide premium nutritional care. With a unique combination of nutrients, and vitamin C which contributes to normal collagen formation for the normal function of bone and cartilage.

Jointace® Vitabiotics
nutritional support for an active life

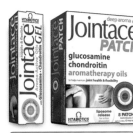
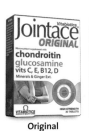

Original

with Omega-3

Collagen

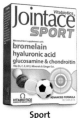
Max

Sport

Fizz

also GEL or PATCH
for direct application.
Ideal alongside *Jointace®* Tabs or Caps.

From *Boots*, Superdrug, supermarkets, Lloydspharmacy, chemists, Holland & Barrett, GNC, health stores & *www.jointace.com*

Vitamin supplements may benefit those with nutritionally inadequate diets.

Voted Favourite
Supplement in its class
by Boots Customers

Boots
Most
loved
vitamins as
voted by you

Britain's leading
supplements
for specific life stages

Ω VITABIOTICS
SCIENCE OF HEALTHY LIVING

Welcome

Are you looking for healthy, diet-friendly recipes and nutrition advice? You've come to the right place. A must for any budding healthy chef, this book from the experts at *Health & Fitness* magazine draws together 50 of our best recipes to satisfy your tastebuds and help you reach your weight-loss goals. You'll learn the secrets to a healthy diet and discover how easy it is to create slimline versions of your favourite meals. You'll also learn some healthy cooking skills to use in the kitchen and discover new, tasty and nutritious ingredients, thanks to expert tips from *H&F*'s healthy chef Lyndon Gee. By following our easy eating suggestions, in combination with regular exercise, you'll soon feel slim, energised and brimming with health. That's a promise!

A balanced diet

Eating a healthy diet not only makes you feel good, it has a wealth of additional benefits. Your eyes sparkle, your skin glows, you can think more clearly and, most importantly, you reduce your risk of serious health conditions, including high blood pressure, high cholesterol, diabetes and cancer. Add to this soaring energy levels and a stable weight, and it sounds like the wonder drug we've all being waiting for. But what exactly is a balanced diet? Read on to discover the secrets to optimum nutrition.

Eat right, stay slim

Want to boost your nutrition or lose weight? Here's how

Contrary to what you may have read, seen on TV or been told in the past, a balanced diet is easy to achieve. Variety and portion control is the key. You should eat a well-proportioned amount of all food groups to ensure you get all the levels of macronutrients and micronutrients your body needs to function at its best (see box). A healthy diet may help to prevent certain illnesses, such as heart disease, stroke and diabetes. It may also help to reduce your risk of developing some cancers. Your immune system thrives on healthy foods, so eating a balanced diet may help you to recover faster from colds and flu. Also, if you are overweight and would like to drop pounds, eating a healthy diet can help you achieve that. Whatever your goal is, a balanced diet is your best plan of attack in the long term.

PORTION CONTROL

If you're already eating a balanced diet and want to lose weight, check you're not over-eating. The problem with modern fad diets is they do not address the amount we're eating, but advise you to cut certain food groups out of your diet in order to achieve quick weight-loss results. For example, the

You should eat a well-proportioned amount of all the food groups, to get the nutrients your body needs

Atkins Diet and Dukan Diet both restrict carbohydrate intake. But, to manage your weight in the long term and achieve optimum health, a diet containing all food groups – unrefined starchy foods such as potatoes, rice and pasta; plenty of fruit and vegetables; some protein-rich foods such as meat, fish and beans; some milk and dairy foods; not too much fat, salt or sugar – is the best way to give your body all the nutrients it needs. If you restrict a food group, you're less likely to consume a balance of all the necessary nutrients for health and wellbeing. Plus, you're also likely to develop cravings for the foods you've been avoiding. Simply cutting down – not cutting out – is the answer.

KNOW YOUR NUTRIENTS

MACRONUTRIENTS
The nutrients needed in large quantities every day. Protein, carbohydrate and fat form the foundation of your diet.

MICRONUTRIENTS
These are found in smaller amounts in food and include vitamins and minerals. Fibre and water, although they don't contain nutrients or provide the body with energy, are also classed as micronutrients, because each forms an essential part of your diet.

All foods contain macro- and micronutrients in varying quantities. For example, a slice of white bread and a slice of wholemeal bread contain similar amounts of carbohydrate, but wholemeal bread contains more vitamins, minerals and fibre than its white counterpart. Your body gets more bang for its buck with wholemeal bread! For this reason, it's important to eat a varied diet, with as much fresh and unprocessed food as possible.

The Eatwell Plate

Follow these simple guidelines to ensure your diet contains all the nutrients your body needs

There's an easy way to make sure you achieve a balanced diet and the optimum proportions for each food group. The Food Standards Agency (FSA) has developed the Eatwell Plate to explain the foods that make up a balanced diet. It's a useful tool for planning your meals and managing portion sizes. The plate represents your own plate at mealtimes, and helps you to understand what percentage of your total daily energy needs should come from each food group. It is split into five key food groups.

1. FRUIT AND VEGETABLES
One third of your daily food intake (or your plate at mealtimes) should consist of fruit and vegetables. Aim to eat at least five portions (three vegetables and two pieces of fruit) each day. As well as fresh fruit and veg, frozen, canned, dried or juiced produce count, too. Aim for two portions of vegetables at every meal and have a piece of fruit as a snack to meet this recommended amount. As potatoes are a starchy carbohydrate, they are not classified as a vegetable.

2. STARCHY CARBOHYDRATES

Bread, pasta, potatoes, rice and other starchy foods should make up a third of your plate. These carbohydrates are a great source of energy, and they also contain essential micronutrients such as calcium, iron and B vitamins, plus fibre to keep your digestive system working smoothly. By opting for wholegrain versions, you will further increase the vitamins and minerals in your diet.

3. DAIRY PRODUCTS

Eat two to three portions of milk or dairy products each day. One fifth of the Eatwell Plate is dedicated to this group, as these foods are a great source of protein, calcium, vitamin A and B12. They can be high in fat, so keep your macronutrients in balance by choosing low-fat versions. For example, cottage cheese is a great replacement for cheddar cheese.

4. FAT AND SUGAR

With a low-nutritional profile, fat and sugar should make up five per cent of your plate. Processed foods such as fizzy drinks or cakes, biscuits and salad dressings, should be consumed in moderation, or reserved as a treat.

5. MEAT, FISH, EGGS AND BEANS

Aim to consume two to three portions of low-fat protein each day. This includes lean meat, fish, beans and other non-dairy sources of protein, such as eggs.

PORTION GUIDES

Do you know your quantities? The following servings are equivalent to 1 portion. Use them as a mealtime guide

✳

1 slice of bread
1/2 baked potato
2 tablespoons cooked rice
3 tablespoons cooked pasta
3 tablespoons breakfast cereal

✳

75g lean meat
75g oily fish
150g white fish
2 medium eggs
4 tablespoons pulses
2 tablespoons nuts

✳

200ml milk
150g yoghurt
30g hard cheese
2 tablespoons cottage cheese

✳

2 slices pineapple
2 small kiwis
large handful berries
150ml fresh juice or smoothie

✳

3 tablespoons cooked vegetables

✳

1 tablespoon olive oil

GLYCAEMIC INDEX & GLYCAEMIC LOAD

The glycaemic index (GI) is the classification of food based on how quickly it is broken down and absorbed into the bloodstream. It's a good indicator of how quickly your food will convert to sugar after eating. Foods are ranked against pure glucose, which is the most easily absorbed form of sugar, and rated 100. If a food is rated less than 55 it deemed low GI and will be slowly absorbed. Oats, wholewheat bread and green vegetables are examples of low-GI foods. Those classed 56-69 are medium GI, and 70-100 are high, meaning they are likely to make your blood sugar spike. Cornflakes, white bread and boiled white potatoes are examples of high-GI foods. Eat a high-GI jam sandwich before you exercise, to give you energy on demand.

GI does not take into account the amount of carbohydrate in a food, however. So glycaemic load (GL) is a better indicator of how a serving of food will affect your blood sugar. For example, watermelon has a high GI of 72, but this is based on the equivalent of five servings of watermelon, so actually one serving is unlikely to have a big effect on your blood sugar levels. Hence watermelon has a low GL of 7. Many foods, such as potatoes, carrots and pineapple, are high GI but low GL and should be consumed because they are loaded with nutrients.

The glycaemic index is a good indicator of how quickly your food will convert to sugar after eating

The energy equation

Here's how to discover your daily calorie needs and stay a healthy weight

T hanks to years of scaremongering and poor advice, calories are feared by many dieters. News flash! Your body needs calories to survive and function at its best, so don't be scared of them.

A calorie is a unit of measurement for the amount of energy your body can get from food. If you're eating a balanced diet but your overall calorie intake exceeds the number of calories you burn off each day through activity, it's hard to maintain your current weight or lose weight.

The number of calories needed each day for the body to function efficiently is different for each individual. Your weight, age and activity level are the main factors that determine your daily calorie requirement.

CALCULATE YOUR CALORIES

Your body requires a certain number of calories each day just to survive. This is called your basal metabolic rate (BMR). In order to perform any other activity – exercise or an active job – your body requires more calories for fuel. This is referred to as your physical activity level (PAL). To find your individual daily calorie requirement, simply multiply your BMR by your PAL rating – see box below.

BASAL METABOLIC RATE (BMR)

Age	BMR male	BMR female
10–17 years	17.7 x weight (kg) + 657	13.4 x weight (kg) + 692
18–29 years	15.1 x weight (kg) + 692	14.8 x weight (kg) + 487
30–59 years	11.5 x weight (kg) + 873	8.3 x weight (kg) + 846
60–74 years	11.9 x weight (kg) + 700	9.2 x weight (kg) + 687

PHYSICAL ACTIVITY LEVEL (PAL)

	WORK ACTIVITY					
	light		moderate		heavy	
NON-WORK	Male	Female	Male	Female	Male	Female
light	1.4	1.4	1.6	1.5	1.7	1.5
moderate	1.5	1.5	1.7	1.6	1.8	1.6
heavy	1.6	1.6	1.8	1.7	1.9	1.7

EXAMPLE

A woman aged 34, weighing 70kg has a BMR of 1,427 calories. (8.3 x 70 + 846 = 1,427 calories) The woman has a sedentary office job, but runs triathlons in her spare time. Her PAL rating is 1.6. By multiplying her BMR by her PAL rating, we can see she needs 2,283 calories each day. (1,427 x 1.6 = 2,283 calories)

If your goal is to lose weight, reduce your recommended daily calorie intake by 500-700 calories

WEIGHT LOSS

This equation (below left) calculates the number of calories you would need to consume every day in order to *maintain* your current weight. If your goal is to lose weight, you should aim to reduce your daily calorie intake by 500-700 calories, which would lead to a manageable weight loss of 1-2lbs (500-900g) each week. If you cut any more calories than this, you will be restricting your diet too much and your energy, concentration and general wellbeing will suffer.

You can cut calories by reducing your food intake and/or by increasing your activity level in order to burn extra calories. A combination of the two is most effective. For example, cut 250 calories from your food intake (eat one less snack or reduce your meal portions slightly) and fit in a power walk or 15-minute workout to burn another 250 calories.

MACRONUTRIENT CALORIES

So you can apply the principles of the Eatwell Plate at meal times, it's important to know your recommended daily calorie intake. Once you have calculated your daily calorie intake, you can then find out how much carbohydrate, protein and fat your diet should include. As a guideline, 50-55 per cent of your energy each day should come from carbohydrates, 30-35 per cent from fat and 10-15 per cent from protein. In each gramme of protein and carbohydrate there are four calories. In one gramme of fat there are nine calories. By doing this, you can make sure you're eating the right balance of macronutrients, without exceeding your calorie intake.

EXAMPLE

If your recommended daily calorie intake is 2,000 calories, this breaks down into:
- carbs   1,000-1,100 cals   (250-275g)
- fats   600-700 cals   (67-78g)
- protein 200-300 cals   (50-75g)

Know your enemy

Fat, sugar and salt have their place in a balanced diet, but enjoy them in moderation

Fat, sugar and salt are classified as the baddies in modern diets. Eaten in excess they can be detrimental to your health, but kept to a minimum the trio still have a place in a healthy eating plan. Most heavily processed foods contain unhealthy amounts of fat, sugar and salt – a ready meal is likely to contain more of these nutritional nasties compared to the same meal cooked from scratch in your kitchen. Unfortunately, fat, sugar and salt send your taste buds into a frenzy, meaning when you have a little, you just want more! But, there are two sides to every story so we've demystified these diet demons to help you make the best choices.

Fat

Fat plays an important role in the body – it gives you energy, keeps you insulated and protects and repairs cells. It is, however, the most calorie-dense macronutrient, with nine calories per gramme. Too much in your diet can be as bad for your health as it is for your waistline. It is linked to greater risk of heart disease, high blood pressure and type 2 diabetes. But fat comes in many forms – some healthy and others not – so check you're eating the right sort.

Sugar

Most people eat too much sugar. It's a stimulant and addictive, so cutting down can be tricky as your body demands its sweet fix. Sugar plays havoc with your brain's neurotransmitters – when you eat it, your brain's reward signals begin to fire and your ability to exercise self-control is compromised. But sugar is a great instant fuel source, particularly if you're exercising regularly. Stick to naturally sweet foods, such as fruit, instead of gorging on heavily processed sugars.

Salt

Adults should consume no more than 6g of salt per day – equivalent to one teaspoon. Just as with fat and sugar, salt is often demonised. Studies link high dietary levels to high blood pressure, increased risk of heart disease and stroke. But it's an essential part of your diet, too. Every cell in your body is dependent on sodium (salt in the body); it helps regulate blood sugar levels, is necessary for proper hydration and helps muscle recovery after exercise. Get your salt balance right and good health will follow.

THE GOOD Unsaturated fats – monounsaturated and polyunsaturated – are the healthiest fats to include in your diet. Although they should be enjoyed in moderation, they're considered beneficial for lowering levels of harmful cholesterol and they lessen the risk of heart disease. Find them in oily fish, nuts and seeds, sunflower and olive oil and avocados. Omega-3 fatty acids, found in salmon and flaxseeds, are very good for heart health.

THE BAD Fatty meat, cheese, butter, cream, biscuits and cakes all contain saturated fat which can increase levels of bad cholesterol in the blood and your risk of heart disease. Aim to eat no more than 20g of saturated fat each day.

THE UGLY Trans fats are found in very low levels in natural foods, but in high quantities in processed foods. Give products containing hydrogenated vegetable oils (polyunsaturated fats that have been processed) a wide berth as they are particularly bad for your health and the body struggles to eliminate them or put them to good use. Margarines, spreads, crisps, baked goods and fast food are the usual culprits.

THE GOOD Sugar occurs naturally in many healthy foods. Fruit and milk contain natural sugars (fructose and lactose, respectively) and these shouldn't be restricted in your diet. The sugars found in fruit and natural yoghurt are less likely to play havoc with your blood sugar levels. A handful of berries, chopped apple or a pot of natural yoghurt with some mixed seeds makes the ideal snack.

THE BAD Whether you're a dessert person or a cupcake queen, you can still be a virtuous chef. Natural sweeteners such as stevia, agave nectar, xylitol, raw honey and coconut nectar can be used in place of cane sugar in recipes. These sweet solutions usually contain fewer calories and are sweeter than regular sugar so you can use less. Mashed bananas, dates and other dried fruits are great sugar replacements, too.

THE UGLY Artificial sweeteners and fructose found in processed foods are a big no-no. Avoid fizzy drinks, biscuits, cakes, sweets and many low-fat diet foods as these can contain high levels of refined fructose. Excessive consumption can lead to insulin resistance (a symptom of type 2 diabetes), water retention, diarrhoea and poor vitamin and mineral absorption. It also puts you at risk of high cholesterol, high blood pressure and obesity.

THE GOOD White table salt isn't your only option for salt – there are plenty of healthier options on the market, containing the full spectrum of minerals and nutrients to enhance your health. Himalayan Crystal Salt for example is an unrefined salt containing 84 minerals (table salt has four) and is salt as nature intended.

THE BAD You don't have to add salt to your food to be getting too much in your diet. The more processed food you eat, the more you'll be consuming. Everyday foods such as bread, cereal and processed meats contain surprisingly high amounts of salt. Always check food labels – high levels of salt are 1.5g per 100g (0.6g sodium).

THE UGLY Table salt, because it's so heavily refined, contains fewer healthy minerals compared to raw salt, including the vital mineral, iodine. This is necessary to prevent degenerative illnesses, so most refined salts are fortified with iodine after processing. Do not buy 'sea salt' thinking you're buying a healthier alternative to table salt. All salt comes from the sea, so the phrase is meaningless. Maldon Salt, Celtic Sea Salt and Welsh Halen Môn contain the most minerals.

Be your own nutritionist

Keeping a food diary is a great way to help you stay on track

Great snacks!

D o you wish you had a nutritionist to help you lose weight and get your diet in order? The good news is you can become your own diet mentor – all you need is a piece of paper and a pen. Research shows you can double your weight-loss efforts by keeping a food diary, and you can clean up your eating habits, too.

Studies show that writing down everything you eat and drink at least six days a week could increase your weight-loss potential. Most people underestimate the amount they eat by up to 50 per cent, so jotting down everything you eat will make you a more accountable dieter.

It's useful to analyse what, when and why you eat. By keeping a food diary you'll be less likely to eat mindlessly, and should find sticking to your daily calorie goal a lot easier. It will also show if you're getting a balance of macronutrients – protein, fats and carbohydrates – as well as a variety of micronutrients – vitamins, minerals, water and fibre. Plus, it will flag up when you're most likely to over-eat, skip meals and snack.

GETTING STARTED

❂ Decide how you would like to record your food diary. Pen and paper works for most people, but you can also use online diaries and mobile phone apps such as My Fitness Pal (myfitnesspal.com) or Pure Lifestyle (purelifestyle.co.uk), which will also provide some nutritional analysis for you.
❂ On day one, write down your starting weight. Then make a commitment to record everything you eat, as soon as you eat it. If you rely on memory at the end of the day it's likely you'll underestimate portions or forget something!

	EXERCISE	DRINKS	MEAL	FOOD & AMOUNT EATEN	TIME	MOOD	HUNGER LOW - 1 HIGH - 5
DAY 1			Breakfast				
			Snack				
			Lunch				
			Snack				
			Dinner				
			Other				

WHAT TO RECORD

To reap the benefits of using a food diary, record as much information as possible but you must be honest!

FOOD Record all food including any sweeteners, condiments, added salt and sauces – as these all add calories. Refer to the Eatwell Plate to check your energy and nutrient balance. For example, at breakfast check that you have included a good source of protein, as this will keep you feeling fuller for longer, stabilise your blood sugar levels and stop you snacking in the day. Are you having two portions of fruit and at least three portions of vegetables every day? One portion of fruit or vegetables is roughly 80g. Are you eating two portions of oily fish or flaxseeds per week to get sufficient omega-3 essential fatty acids into your diet? If you're not pregnant, breastfeeding or hoping to start a family in the future, you can have up to four portions a week, according to the NHS. Keep an eye on portion sizes by weighing your food. Or if this is too time-consuming, you can record rough measurements, such as a tablespoon, a cup or a handful. Check you are eating a range of vegetables, starchy carbohydrates and lean protein sources to benefit from a broader range of vitamins and minerals.

DRINKS If you have milk in your coffee, or some wine on a Friday night, write this down. Alcohol contains seven calories per gramme. If you have a cocktail, note the calories from the alcohol and mixers. Keeping a record of your fluid intake will help maintain good hydration, too. The Foods Standards Agency recommends six to eight glasses of water per day (1.5 to 2 litres). If you're exercising, drink an extra 1ml of water for every calorie you burn, so, if you burn 500 calories at the gym, drink an additional 500ml water.

COOKING METHODS Each tablespoon of olive oil adds 100 calories to your meal so try dry-frying or grilling your steak or salmon fillet. Remove excess fat or skin from meat and poultry and opt for low-fat dairy options. Microwave or steam vegetables to retain more of their nutrients instead of using butter or oil.

HUNGER If you're hungry, you will find a diet hard to sustain. By rating your hunger between one and five, you can make wiser food choices to keep you fuller for longer. You're more likely to feel satiated when you've had a meal containing a source of protein and fibre, for example nutty muesli topped with natural live yoghurt.

FEELINGS Emotional eating is a big problem when it comes to managing weight, especially for women. If you're bored, stressed, angry or even happy, bigger portions and the wrong food choices become more appealing. Write down what you eat and how you felt at the time, to highlight problem areas.

TIME Are you eating extra calories outside of mealtimes? When you skipped breakfast, did you have a calorific snack? Write down where you were when you ate, too, because we associate different situations with eating. For example, when you go to the cinema, take a pot of fruit to munch on, instead of sweets or fattening popcorn.

EXERCISE To lose weight, you need to increase your current level of activity. Aim for 30-60 minute physical exercise five days a week. On the days you exercise, you may need to eat a few more calories but fuel up on protein, not extra carbs, to reduce muscle soreness.

SELF-EVALUATION

❋

Your diary will highlight skipped meals and long periods left between meals. Check you're eating no more than three meals and one or two snacks a day.

❋

At the end of the week, weigh yourself again and make a note of your new weight. Depending on whether you have lost or gained weight, you can make a realistic assessment of your food diary. If you have lost weight, ask yourself what you did that was good that week. Also look out for patterns – when are you most hungry? Do you eat when you're stressed or bored?

❋

Reward progress, with a non-food treat – a magazine, a beauty treatment or a new outfit are great ways to give yourself a pat on the back.

The perfect snack

When hunger strikes, give your body what it needs – not that piece of chocolate cake!

S nack attacks can be your downfall when you're watching your weight. If you work in an office, for example, you could be eating around 650 calories each day through snacking alone! Whether it's the habit of eating a biscuit with your cup of tea, or mindlessly eating when food is in your field of vision, boredom, stress, reward and your colleagues' eating behaviours play a huge part in your snacking tendencies. Recognise these factors and you can start to make conscious decisions about what you eat and when.

DON'T *skip meals*

Skip meals and you're more likely to binge later in the day. It's yet another good reason to start the day with an energising breakfast followed by a healthy carb- and protein-filled lunch, such as a tuna bean salad. You'll then have enough control to stick to a healthy meal of 400 calories, with some leeway for a few guilt-free treats in the evening.

DON'T *cave in to cravings*

One strategy to manage blood sugar dips is to eat foods low on the glycaemic index (GI). Snacks such as oatcakes topped with cottage cheese or an apple and a handful of nuts are low-GI. When you do indulge, keep sweet treats to meal times, as they will affect your blood sugar levels less.

DO *eat breakfast*

A protein-rich breakfast with slow-releasing carbohydrates will fill you up and stop you reaching for elevenses. A poached egg on wholemeal toast, or granola topped with yoghurt will ramp up your protein intake. If you aren't hungry first thing, it's fine to wait, but raiding the biscuit tin doesn't count as breakfast!

✳
*Ramp up the fibre
and protein content
of your snacks
to make you feel
fuller for longer*

**HEALTHY
SNACKS**
Try these snack
suggestions to beat
cravings and avoid
diet sabotage

❋
Half an avocado
= **140 calories**
Full of fibre and
essential fats.

❋
One apple and
20g almond butter
= **175 calories**
Almond butter contains
magnesium, vitamin E
and calcium.

❋
One hard-boiled egg
= **70 calories**
Contains healthy fats and
6.5g protein.

❋
90g edamame beans
= **120 calories**
36 per cent protein
and high in fibre.

❋
150g natural yoghurt
with berries/seeds
= **185 calories**
A 25g serving of seeds
contains 6g protein.

❋
Crudités & houmous
= **160 calories**
50g low-fat houmous contains
125 calories. Carrots contain
37 calories per 100g.

DO *prepare snacks*
When packing your lunch for work, add two
snacks of roughly 200 calories each. They
should be well-constructed mini-meals,
and contain fibre, protein, carbohydrate
and healthy fat. Half an avocado, or two
plums and half a dozen walnuts would be
great choices.

DO *keep food out of sight*
Banish snacks to your desk drawer and
clear your kitchen worktops of all snack
foods. Instead, have a bottle of water
in view at all times. Each time you have
a snack attack, take a sip of water. Plus,
switch your caffeine fixes to herbal tea to
boost your hydration.

Supermarket savvy

Navigate the aisles like a pro and you'll come away with the healthiest choices at the best price

Everyone loves to shop, but when you're on a diet or counting the pennies, going food shopping can be stressful. Supermarkets play marketing tricks on us at every turn of the trolley. Making a list in advance and not shopping on an empty stomach go without saying, but the temptation of end-of-aisle offers, the smell of freshly baked bread and the sound of classical music are all ploys to make you part with cash and lose your healthy eating focus. Here's our guide to surviving the temptations and shopping healthily, on a budget.

1 BUY LOCAL

Scan the fruit and vegetable aisles for locally grown produce. When fresh fruit and vegetables are imported from far-flung locations, their nutrient density is compromised. The Food Standards Agency (FSA) found some frozen vegetables, such as broccoli, contain more nutrients than 'fresh' vegetables if they've travelled in poorly-refrigerated conditions for 1,000 miles or more.

Produce such as apples and potatoes may have been left in storage for up to six months before they make it to the shelves, while spinach loses between 50 and 90 per cent of its vitamin C within 24 hours of picking when stored at room temperature.

Supporting local farmers and buying their produce will save you money and help reduce air pollution, too. Plus, because their fruit and

Shop wisely and you will still be able to eat a nutritious diet without blowing your budget

veg will be seasonal, you will enjoy a variety of produce all year round.

2 KEEP TO THE PERIMETER

Sticking to the outer aisles of the supermarket will help you fill your trolley with healthy goods. Here you'll find unprocessed, natural food items, such as fresh meat, fish, vegetables and fruit. Choose a rainbow of vegetables. A variety of colour will ensure you eat a wide range of antioxidant-rich phytonutrients. Supermarkets often place everyday products such as fresh milk at the back of the store, so you have to walk down the aisles and past all the tempting offers. So, next time you spy signs saying 'confectionary', 'crisps' or 'soft drinks', walk straight past. These aisles contain high-fat and high-sugar foods.

3 THINK LONG-LIFE

Check out the canned sections for nutritious, long-life foods. Fish on the fresh counter can be expensive unless there's a special offer, but canned salmon, sardines and mackerel are a cheaper alternative, and will help you reach your quota of oily fish for less. Look for fish in spring water, rather than oil, with no added salt. The same goes for pulses. Buy chickpeas, lentils and beans to add bulk and fibre to dishes, without spending too much on meat. Look for fruit canned in its own juice rather than syrup as an easy way to reach your five-a-day, without adding extra calories.

4 GO NATURAL

Try to avoid food products that contain more than five ingredients or those you can't pronounce, as they're probably overly processed. Processed foods provide fewer nutrients and are less likely to satiate your hunger. For example, refined or instant oatmeal takes less time to digest than plain rolled oats, so you'll be seeking snacks by mid-morning. Opt for 100 per cent fruit juice and 100 per cent wholegrain foods to get more vitamins and minerals.

5 EXPLORE THE FREE-FROM AISLE

Typically, foods in the 'free-from' aisle contain a wider variety of healthy ingredients. Cereal bars are a classic example – they're likely to contain extra nuts, seeds, dried fruit, oats and healthy grains. Remember though, just because a food is free from one ingredient, doesn't mean the rest of the ingredients are healthy. A cake might not contain wheat, but it could still be packed with fat and sugar.

6 GET SHELF SAVVY

Reach to the back of the shelves for fresher fruit, salad, veg, dairy, meat and eggs. Remember, sell-by dates are there for the supermarkets to use. If your vegetables are past their sell-by date, this doesn't necessarily mean they're riddled with mould, so don't waste them. Supermarkets also place the products with the greatest profit margin – or brands who can pay for the best positioning – at eye level. Small-scale, health food producers don't have big budgets, so make an effort to seek them out.

7 AVOID BOGOFS

Unless offers and discounts relate to healthy store cupboard items, resist the temptation to buy them – you will eat that family-sized pack of cookies if you buy it! If you're tempted by 'Buy-one-get-one-free' offers on salad and vegetables, think when you'll use them, as the use-by dates are often short. Some multiple-buy offers may only save 5p – not really worth it if you end up chucking them, or worse, over-eating. If your veggies start to lose their freshness, make soups and freeze them.

FIVE-A-DAY ON A BUDGET

One-in-six people say rising food prices make it difficult to eat healthily. So how can you get your five-a-day and stay within your budget?

✳

Make simple swaps

Snack on fruit and veg to reach your five-a-day and save money. An apple from the market costs on average 25p, compared with chocolate (60p) or a packet of crisps (50p).

✳

Seek out bargains

The 'express' or 'local' supermarkets will charge more than their larger stores. Plus, buying fruit and vegetables loose rather than pre-packed is usually cheaper. Browse the reduced aisle for goods close to their 'sell-by' date. 'Best-before' foods are still edible, but avoid foods past their 'use-by' date.

✳

Try canned

Canned tomatoes and tomato soup are the best sources of the antioxidant lycopene, thought to reduce some types of cancer. Canned foods have a long shelf life because the food is cooked in the can, locking all the nutrition inside without the need for preservatives.

✳

Check the freezer

Frozen green veg can contain more nutrients than fresh. After eight days in a fridge, spinach has lost 47 per cent of its folic acid and other nutrients are in rapid decline. The frozen version – usually frozen on the day it's picked – will be far more nutritious. Frozen peas and beans are other good choices.

✳

Box clever

Register for a veg box scheme with your local farmer to eat seasonal produce at a fraction of the cost. The Seasons Vegbox from Riverford Organic (riverford.co.uk) costs £13.45 and contains eight to 10 varieties of fruit and veg, which feeds three adults for a week.

Menu planning

Plan your week's meals seven days ahead to avoid diet meltdowns

A t the beginning of every week, before you head to the supermarket, take some time to plan your meals for the next seven days. Not only will this save you time, wasted food and cash at the till, but you'll find it easier to stick to your new healthy diet, too. With a well-stocked fridge you're less likely to make last-minute trips to the shops for quick-fix meals, which will often be high in empty calories. Organisation, preparation and motivation are the buzzwords for sticking with healthy eating.

HOW TO DO IT
Set aside some time each week to organise your menus. Write out a week's timetable of meals in a notebook (see right). Fill in your menus, allocating more complicated dishes for when you have more time. Could you prepare lunches in a batch? Or make double portions so there's enough for the next day? On nights you'll be late at work or going to the gym, you could eat leftovers. If you're time-starved, plan meals that take less than 30 minutes to prepare or invest in a slow cooker to have a meal ready when you get home.

YOUR HEALTHY SHOPPING LIST

Take this checklist with you when you shop, to ensure your store cupboard is filled with a balance of nutrients. Add your favourites if they're not already on the list.

✔ Food cupboard
Wholewheat bread, pitta, wraps and pasta
Brown rice
Canned pulses:
    kidney beans,
    chickpeas,
    cannellini beans
Lentils
Canned tomatoes
Popping corn
Plain rolled oats
Unsalted, raw nuts:
    cashews, almonds,
    walnuts
Quinoa
Dried spices & herbs:
    tumeric, cumin, chilli
    flakes, oregano

✔ Oils
Avocado oil
Olive oil
Coconut oil
Rapeseed oil

✔ Frozen
Frozen yoghurt
Frozen vegetables:
    peas, spinach,
    broad beans
Frozen fruit:
    berries, mango,
    pineapple
Prawns, white fish,
salmon fillets

✔ Fresh
Fruit:
    experiment each
    week with snacking
    fruits, and buy
    lemons and limes to
    flavour water and
    make dressings
Vegetables:
    buy a rainbow:
    greens, reds,
    oranges, yellows
    and purples
Salad:
    choose high-nutrient
    leaves such as
    spinach, watercress
    and rocket
Herbs:
    mint, basil,
    coriander, parsley

Lean meat & poultry:
    free range and
    organic preferable
Fish and seafood
Eggs:
    free range and
    organic preferable
Low-fat natural
yoghurt and crème
fraîche
Low-fat cheese:
    cottage cheese,
    Parmesan

TOP TIP
Stick your completed menu planner on your fridge for quick reference

	BREAKFAST	LUNCH	DINNER	SNACKS
MONDAY				
TUESDAY				
WEDNESDAY				
THURSDAY				
FRIDAY				
SATURDAY				
SUNDAY				

How to decipher food labels

Beat the marketing jargon to stick to your healthy diet

Do you feel bamboozled by the lingo used by food manufacturers to sell their 'healthy' products? Food labels have long been attacked for being confusing, but they can also be misleading. For instance, under European Union law, a 'low-fat' product must contain three per cent or less fat per 100g, but 'lower-fat' products can contain more.

Part of the problem is that food labels are selective with the truth, using a few carefully chosen words and colours to make us think we're buying superfoods. Baked beans may provide one of your five-a-day but some brands also contain the recommended daily allowance of salt for a woman and more than the daily allowance for a child. Some cream cheese slices claim to be a 'good source of calcium', but they also contain more than 20 per cent fat – there are other sources of calcium that won't put added strain on your bathroom scales.

WHAT THE LAW SAYS

Food labels bombard us with health claims, ingredients and numbers. Yet legally, they only have to include energy, protein, carbohydrate and fat content. The voluntary traffic light system was introduced by the Food Standards Agency (FSA) in 2004 and colour codes nutritional information to show if the food has high (red), medium (amber) or low (green) amounts of fat, saturated fat, sugars and salt.

USE YOUR LOAF

Much of the nutritional information on the back of products is meaningless. The figures you should always check are sugar, fat, salt and calorie content. Remember nutritional values are often shown per 100g, rather than portion size (which will often exceed 100g). For instance, if you buy a pizza, you'll probably eat a whole one while the calorie figure given may be per slice, or based on two sharing.

YOUR DAILY INTAKE SHOULD NOT EXCEED		
Energy:	8,400kJ/2,000kcal	
Total fat:		70g
Saturated fat:		20g
Sugars:		90g
Salt:		6g

WHAT THE FIGURES MEAN

Per portion of food, follow these guidelines:

TOTAL FAT
High: more than 17.5g of fat per 100g
Low: 3g of fat or less per 100g

SATURATED FAT
High: more than 5g of saturated fat per 100g
Low: 1.5g of saturated fat or less per 100g

SUGARS
High: more than 22.5g of total sugars per 100g
Low: 5g of total sugars or less per 100g

SALT
High: more than 1.5g of salt per 100g (or 0.6g sodium)
Low: 0.3g of salt or less per 100g (or 0.1g sodium)

NUTRITION		
Typical values	100g contains	Each pack (400g) contains
Energy	389kJ	1,556kJ
	93kcal	370kcal
Protein	3.4g	13.6g
Carbohydrate	12.3g	49.2g
of which sugars	3.0g	12.0g
starch	3.3g	13.2g
Fat	3.3g	13.2g
of which saturates	1.7g	6.8g
mono-unsaturates	1.1g	4.4g
polyunsaturates	0.3g	1.2g
Fibre	2.0g	8.0g
Sodium	0.2g	0.7g
Salt equivalent	0.5g	1.8g

LEARN THE LINGO

Here's what the blurb on your healthy, fat-free, light tub of margarine with added vitamins really means:

'Light or lite'
It may imply 'low fat', but this is just marketing speak. A product must contain less than 3g of fat per 100g to qualify as 'low fat', according to the FSA and the EU. One popular 'light' brand of spread contains 16g/100g, and even the extra light variety comes in at 5g!

'Fat free'
The Consumers' Association highlighted the confusing use of this term by singling out a popular fruit loaf, which trumpets the claim '90 per cent fat free'. Simple mathematics reveals the product is therefore a relatively high 10 per cent fat. 'Virtually fat free' is even worse, in that it might as well say, 'not fat free'.

'With added vitamins'
Vitamins may be added in microscopic amounts giving minimal benefit. Some products, such as bread, yoghurt, milk and cereals are fortified with vitamins and can make a significant contribution to your nutritional status. But, nutritionally enhanced foods are essentially the same as taking a vitamin supplement.

'Healthy'
Claims such as 'healthy' or 'good for you', are only allowed if approved by the European Food Safety Authority. Labels can't claim that food can treat, prevent or cure any disease or medical condition – these claims can only be made by licensed medicines.

In the kitchen

Keeping a well-stocked and organised kitchen will minimise temptation and keep your healthy eating plan on track. A full, prominently placed fruit bowl will help you get your five-a-day, while placing the biscuit barrel out of sight will stop mindless snacking. Your kitchen should be a place that's conducive to creating tasty, nutritious meals in a flash, so having essential store cupboard ingredients to hand is a good place to start.

Swap that... for this!

← OLIVE OIL / SUNFLOWER OIL →

Monounsaturated oils, such as olive oil and avocado oil, have a low smoke point, so they become unstable when heated to high temperatures. Save for drizzling on salads. For cooking, use a small amount of polyunsaturated oil, such as sunflower or grapeseed.

← SUGAR / STEVIA →

Stevia is a plant-derived natural sweetener containing minimal calories. It doesn't have the same insulin-spiking effect as regular sugar, and can be used in the same way when cooking. When baking, even a mashed banana can be used as a sugar alternative.

← CHEDDAR CHEESE / GRUYÈRE CHEESE →

Cheese is great for flavouring dishes but it's high in salt and saturated fat. For dishes such as risotto or cauliflower cheese, opt for strong-tasting varieties such as Gruyère or Parmesan instead of Cheddar. Lower fat ricotta adds creaminess without the fat.

← SALT / LEMON JUICE →

A squeeze of lemon juice at the end of cooking mimics the taste of salt without the blood-pressure raising side-effects. A splash of vinegar or olive oil can also trick your tastebuds. Always taste your food before adding salt during the cooking process.

SPICE UP YOUR LIFE!

Inject flavour into your dishes with these health-promoting ingredients

Paprika
This bright red spice comes from sweet and hot dried peppers and contains three times the vitamin C of oranges, and capsaicin, an anti-inflammatory used to treat joint pain.
Use it: Sprinkle over popcorn, or potato wedges.

Ginger
Ginger is recognised for its ability to relax blood vessels and stimulate blood flow. It can also be used as remedy for nausea, digestive discomfort and morning sickness.
Use it: Add boiling water to 1 tsp ground ginger to make tea.

A healthy diet shouldn't lack flavour. By substituting ingredients that are high in fat, sugar and salt, with some delicious alternatives, you can cut calories without compromising taste and still be able to enjoy your favourite dishes – guilt-free

⇐ BUTTER / AVOCADO ⇒

Make healthier sandwiches by spreading your bread with mashed avocado or natural yoghurt. Processed margarines or spreads can contain hydrogenated fats so choose a small amount of unsalted, grass-fed butter instead. Avocado can also replace mayonnaise.

⇐ BREADCRUMBS / OATS ⇒

Oats are full of fibre and are a great replacement for breadcrumbs on fish or chicken. Simply coat in a little egg then roll in fine oats until completely covered. Place on greaseproof paper and bake until cooked through and crispy on the outside.

⇐ PASTA / VEGETABLES ⇒

Get handy with your julienne knife or peeler to make vegetable alternatives to spaghetti. You'll reduce the calorie portion of your evening meal and find it easier to reach your five-a-day.

⇐ COUSCOUS / QUINOA ⇒

Couscous is nutritionally similar to pasta as it is made from the same cracked durum wheat. Bulgar wheat, barley and quinoa are healthier grains to use as they contain more vitamins, minerals and protein.

Turmeric	**Saffron**	**Cinnamon**
Its active ingredient, curcumin, is proven to help reduce inflammation, cleanse the blood, heal wounds, increase circulation and also has anti-cancer properties. **Use it:** Sprinkle 1 tsp turmeric into stir-fries and curries.	Used in Chinese medicine to treat heart problems, PMS and for its mood-enhancing benefits, antioxidant-rich saffron can also protect your eyes from harmful UV rays. **Use it:** Add to paella or seafood stew for colour and flavour.	This spice helps balance blood sugar levels and reduce food cravings. Studies link it with improved insulin sensitivity and lower cholesterol. **Use it:** Add to smoothies or almonds before toasting.

Cook smart

Become a healthy gourmet by trying these calorie-saving cooking techniques

P reparing healthy meals from scratch will go a long way to helping you reach your weight-loss goals, especially if you use the right cooking techniques. For instance, you should aim to limit your calories from fat to no more than 30-35 per cent of your total daily calorie intake – that's between 600 and 700 calories (based on a woman's 2,000 daily calorie allowance). However, each tablespoon of oil you use for frying adds more than 100 calories to your dish. By roasting or grilling instead, you not only eliminate added fat, but fat in the food also drips away. This is just one food-prep trick that retains flavour while increasing your meals' healthy credentials. Read on for more solutions.

STEAMING

One of the healthiest cooking techniques is steaming food in a perforated basket above simmering liquid. You can also use an electric steamer or microwave. If you season the water, your food will take on the flavour as it cooks. Ideal for all vegetables, fish fillets and poultry.

STIR-FRYING

A traditional Asian method, stir-frying quickly cooks small, uniform-sized pieces of food while they're rapidly stirred in a wok or large non-stick frying pan. You only need only a small amount of oil or cooking spray for this cooking method; the trick is to keep the ingredients moving and the temperature high.

GRILLING

Exposing food to direct heat under the grill is a fast way to cook. To keep it healthy, cook your meat or oily fish on a wire rack so any fat can drip underneath. For smaller items, such as chopped vegetables, use foil or a long-handled grill basket to prevent pieces from slipping through the rack. Lightly brush vegetables with oil to prevent burning. When grilling fish, switch on your oven-top fan to reduce the fishy smell.

POACHING

To poach foods, gently simmer the ingredients in enough water (use broth or juice for added flavour) to cover until they're cooked through and tender. This is ideal for eggs, fish and poultry. For stove-top poaching, choose a pan that best fits the size and shape of the food so that you need a minimal amount of liquid. It will need a secure lid.

BRAISING

Using a heavy-bottom pan, first seal in the flavour of your meat by quickly frying it in a little oil on a high heat on the stove. Then, cover the meat in a small amount of water or broth and cover the pan before cooking slowly in the oven. In some recipes, the remaining cooking liquid is used to make a flavoursome, nutrient-rich sauce. The best pots for braising are cast iron ones.

Make every meal an occasion. Set the table. Eat with your family. Give yourself the opportunity to enjoy your food without distractions such as TV.

TOP TIP
Spend a little time on presentation. You're more likely to enjoy a meal if it looks as good as it tastes.

BAKING

Besides breads and desserts, you can bake seafood, poultry, lean meat, vegetables and fruits. Place your food in a pan or dish so it's surrounded by the hot, dry air of your oven. Try baking chicken or fish in tinfoil to avoid the fillets drying out, or bake jacket potatoes or wedges in their skins with just a sprinkling of sea salt. Set your oven to between 150°C and 180°C.

ROASTING

Like baking, but at higher temperatures (200°C+) and with quicker cooking times, roasting is a great way to cook meat and vegetables. You can roast foods on a baking sheet without any fat or in a roasting pan. For poultry, oily fish and meat, place a rack inside the roasting pan so that the fat in the food can drip away during cooking. Baste the food regularly to stop it drying out.

SAUTEING

Get your pan very hot and use a small amount of fat to quickly cook strips of beef or chicken and vegetables. Use a good-quality non-stick pan, and you can use less fat. Don't overcrowd the pan and avoid adding water as this will reduce the heat of the pan.

Go, go gadget!

Build your healthy cooking repertoire with a little help from these waistline-friendly kitchen appliances

← A BLENDER

Soups and smoothies are easy to whip up in a blender. Choose from basic models suitable for smoothies, priced from £25 (amazon.co.uk), and more high-tech machines able to make nut milks, sorbets and soups from raw ingredients, which carry a heavier pricetag.
TRY: Vitamix Blender, from £419; vitamix.co.uk

A STEAMER ➣

Steaming is one of the healthiest ways to cook and doesn't require much culinary finesse. Use a steamer – either a metal, bamboo or silicone dish that sits on a saucepan or an electric steamer – to prepare vegetables, fish, chicken or rice.
TRY: Silicone Steamer Set, £17.99; lakeland.co.uk

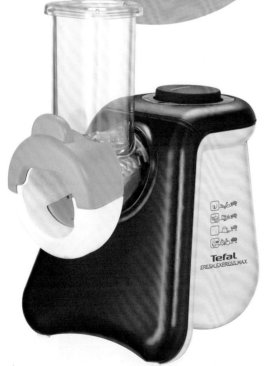

← A LOW-FAT FRYER

Enjoy chips without the guilt with a low-fat fryer, which uses less oil. New models allow you to make a range of meals, from stir-fries to puddings, using healthier oils such as rapeseed, coconut or avocado.
TRY: Tefal Actifry Low-Fat Electric Fryer, £199.99; amazon.co.uk

↑ A FOOD PROCESSOR

Slice, dice, chop, shred and grate your veggies in a flash with a food processor. Pick one that's easy to clean and has a number of serrated blades, to make everything from fresh coleslaw to sliced veggies for stir-fries.
TRY: Tefal Fresh Express Max Food Processor, £79.99; homeandcook.co.uk

SCALES ➡

To fill in your food diary or follow a recipe accurately, a set of scales is necessary. Many kitchen scales will analyse your macronutrient portions and energy intake, too.
TRY: Salter Nutri-Weigh Slim Electronic Scale, £46.99; uk.salterhousewares.com

⬅ A JUICER

Get your five-a-day with a juicer. This gadget separates the liquid from the pulp of your fruit and veg for a concentrated source of vitamins and minerals. Opt for a centrifugal (shredding) or a masticating (chewing) juicer with a powerful motor (1,000 watts +) to get a good yield of juice.
TRY: Sage by Heston Blumenthal The Nutri Juicer, £149.95; johnlewis.com

A HAND BLENDER ➡

Ideal for blending soups, whisking egg whites and making pestos and salsas, a hand-held blender is every cook's must-have. Many come with various attachments and blades to make food prep fast and efficient.
TRY: KitchenAid Hand Blender, £119.95; johnlewis.com

⬅ AN ICE CREAM MAKER

Don't reach for shop-bought ice cream laden with fat and sugar, make your own virtuous sorbet and slimline frozen yoghurt instead. You can experiment with flavours and nutritious ingredients.
TRY: Magimix Ice Cream Maker Glacier 1.5L, £59.99; amazon.co.uk

ACCESSORIES

If you're on a budget, these cheap utensils are a handy addition to any kitchen

Julienne peeler, £3.29; lakeland.co.uk Make fancy vegetable spaghetti or pretty salads with this clever little peeler.

Kuhn Rikon Colori 10cm Paring Knife, £5.95; johnlewis.com These strong and sharp carbon steel blades make easy work of chopping and dicing.

Joseph Joseph Index Advance Chopping Board Set, £46; johnlewis.com For superior kitchen hygiene, avoid cross-contamination by chopping raw and cooked meat, fish and vegetables separately.

Prepara Delux Oil Mist Sprayer, £15.57; amazon.co.uk Make your own flavoured oils and salad dressings and easily control your servings.

Kitchen Craft Prepara Herb Saver, £19.99; amazon.co.uk Keep herbs fresher for longer with this storage system for the fridge.

The recipes

If you want to lose weight and feel energised, it's time to ditch the diet foods and embrace a healthy eating regime. As you've seen, fad diets and long-term calorie restriction don't work. Here's a selection of 50 of our favourite healthy recipes to inspire you to get back in the kitchen. Some of our recipes are slimmer takes on classic dishes, such as Spaghetti bolognese and Sticky toffee pudding. Yes, that's right, you can still enjoy all your favourite foods, but without the guilt.
Happy cooking!

Meet the chef

Healthy gourmet Lyndon Gee, shares his passion for creating
nutritious recipes bursting with flavour

Creating wholesome, healthy food to share with friends in sociable surroundings is a big part of my life. I hope you'll enjoy making some of these recipes and perhaps personalise them by adding your own twist.

Of course, it's essential to make food that tastes great. To me, that's healthy food. I don't feel the need to have high-fat, high-sugar food as a 'treat'. What could be better than natural, seasonal ingredients, simply prepared?

Everyone has favourite foods and flavours. Food unlocks our memories, and my aim is to bring these to life in a healthier, fresher way, without losing the essence of the dish.

I love writing about food and sharing my healthy recipes. And I truly believe it's possible to make healthier food, even for dinner parties or special occasions – the healing properties of food are integral to my dishes. It's rewarding to develop recipes that help people manage or even prevent medical conditions. For optimal wellbeing, we need to ensure our diet contains a wide variety of nutrients.

A CAREER IN THE KITCHEN

I've spent my life working with food, becoming professionally involved at the age of 10 when my parents bought a hotel in the Cotswolds. I loved to help the chefs and learned a lot about fruit and vegetables from the gardener.

This was the life for me, so I went to London to train with the Savoy. After three years' formal training, I worked at Maxims de Paris. Then, to broaden my experience, I became a chef with Antonio Carluccio and Gennaro Contaldo. Their approach was focused on using the very best ingredients, and gave me a love of Italian food and foraging for fungi.

'The healing properties of food are integral to my dishes. It's very rewarding to develop recipes that help people manage or even prevent medical conditions'

have been creating recipes since 2004. I give everyday classic dishes a healthier twist, resulting in great-tasting recipe favourites and a nutrition boost along with flavour!

Now, as a food futurist and working on product development for niche clients and big brands, I'm able to share my enthusiasm for healthy eating and also influence the future of food for consumers.

Lyndon is a fellow of the Institute for Optimum Nutrition, member of the Guild of Food Writers, advisor to the All-Party Parliamentary Group for Entrepreneurship and former vice chair of the Guild of Health Writers; lyndongee.com

When I spent a couple of years in the US running an artisan bakery and restaurant, I became interested in healthy eating as I could see the damage caused by a bad diet – America had an obesity problem long before we did.

HEALTHIER OPTIONS
My wife and I studied nutrition, and I became part of the growing movement towards healthy eating and natural food. We were shareholders in a pioneering organic box scheme and I started to explore ways of creating delicious food with added health benefits – but without losing familiar flavours.

I returned to the UK to take control of catering for Selfridges, with 400 staff feeding more than 10,000 customers every day! It was a big job with a diverse clientele – from drivers in the staff canteen, to celebrities and fashionistas in the Conran-designed restaurant. I created health-boosting gourmet menus and healthier options in all the restaurants.

As a founding director of Slow Food UK, I developed a great interest in food heritage and artisan producers, and to encourage better eating, created two award-winning campaigns promoting healthy local food.

SHARING THE PASSION
In 2001, I started sharing my healthy cooking tips with *Health & Fitness* magazine readers, and

VEGETARIAN DISHES

Boost your vitality with these vitamin-packed superfood dishes

Goat's cheese & red onion pizza

Try this speedy, low-carbohydrate meal, it's perfect after a workout

Serves: 1
Preparation time: 5 minutes
Cooking time: 10 minutes

INGREDIENTS

1 red onion, peeled
1 tsp sunflower oil
Dried oregano
Black pepper
8 cherry tomatoes, halved
1 wholemeal tortilla
30g goat's cheese, thinly sliced
Basil leaves

THE METHOD

1 Pre-heat the oven to 180˚C/gas mark 4. Thinly slice the red onion, add to a pan with a dash of sunflower oil and cook for two to three minutes to soften. Add a good pinch of dried oregano, a generous grind of black pepper and the cherry tomatoes. Mix well and remove from the heat.

2 Place the wholemeal tortilla on a baking sheet and spread the onion and tomato mixture evenly over it. Top with 50g of thinly sliced goat's cheese, broken into pieces.

3 Bake for four to five minutes, or until the cheese starts to melt. Remove from the oven, scatter with roughly torn fresh basil leaves, then serve.

PER SERVING

326	11g	23g	11g	39g	5g	1g
CALORIES	PROTEIN	FAT	SAT FAT	CARBS	FIBRE	SALT

Spaghetti bolognese

Try this healthy vegetarian spin on the UK's favourite pasta dish

Serves: 6
Preparation time:
10 minutes
Cooking time:
30 minutes

INGREDIENTS

A dash of sunflower oil
1 large red onion,
finely chopped
1 carrot, finely diced
½ red pepper, finely chopped
½ yellow pepper, finely
chopped
½ green pepper, finely
chopped
1 courgette, finely diced
2-4 cloves garlic, crushed
1 heaped tsp dried basil
2 heaped tsp dried oregano
Good pinch of salt and plenty
of pepper
A glass of dry wine (white
or red)
2 x 400g can chopped
tomatoes
400g can puy lentils
400g wholemeal spaghetti
A handful of freshly
chopped parsley
Freshly torn basil leaves
Parmesan cheese shavings

METHOD

1 Put the oil in a pan and gently cook the onion until well browned, stirring regularly.

2 Add the carrot, peppers and courgette, and continue to cook gently for 10 minutes, still stirring.

3 Stir in the garlic, dried herbs, salt and pepper, then add the wine, followed by the tomatoes and lentils.

4 Bring to a gentle simmer, cover and cook for 15 minutes, stirring occasionally and adding a little water if too much liquid evaporates and it starts to stick to the pan.

5 Meanwhile, cook the spaghetti according to the instructions on the packet and drain.

6 Add the fresh parsley and basil to a large bowl with the sauce and spaghetti. Mix well and serve with a little Parmesan cheese.

PER SERVING

434	15g	4g	0.5g	57g	13g	0.7g
CALORIES	PROTEIN	FAT	SAT FAT	CARBS	FIBRE	SALT

Fresh herb pesto

Make this nutritious sauce in less time than it takes to cook your pasta

Serves: 4
Preparation time: 10 minutes
Cooking time: 10 minutes

INGREDIENTS

150g mixed fresh herbs – mainly basil and parsley, with a little coriander and mint
100g frozen peas, defrosted
100g rocket leaves, chopped
1 garlic clove, crushed
½ tsp salt
100ml cold-pressed hemp oil
400g dried pasta
Parmesan cheese, finely grated

METHOD

1 Roughly chop the mixed fresh herbs. Add them to a blender with the defrosted frozen peas and chopped rocket leaves and the garlic, salt and cold-pressed hemp oil. Blend well.

2 Cook the pasta according to the instructions on the packet and drain, reserving 50ml of the cooking liquid.

3 Place the pasta in a bowl, then add the pesto and pasta water and toss well. Add plenty of finely grated Parmesan cheese and mix again, then serve.

NUTRI TIP
Try adding a couple of tablespoons of yoghurt or half-fat crème fraîche to make a creamier pesto. For extra texture, flavour and protein in your meal, add sunflower seeds, smoked ham or cooked prawns.

PER SERVING

552	15g	22g	2.5g	77g	5g	0.6g
CALORIES	PROTEIN	FAT	SAT FAT	CARBS	FIBRE	SALT

Sautéed mushrooms with chilli and garlic on chargrilled polenta

Mushrooms add a rich depth of flavour to this healthy dish

Serves: 4
Preparation time: 20 minutes
Cooking time: 6 minutes

INGREDIENTS

200g polenta
500g mixed mushrooms
Dash of olive oil
1 red chilli, de-seeded and finely chopped
3 cloves of garlic, crushed
Parsley, chopped
Dash of white wine
Salt

TOP TIP
Never wash mushrooms, they absorb water. Brush or wipe with damp kitchen paper instead.

METHOD

1 Cook the polenta according to the instructions on the packet, then put it into a container to cool. When needed, slice and griddle for a few minutes on each side.

2 Meanwhile, clean the mixed mushrooms and slice or break them into roughly even-sized pieces. You can use open-cup, button, beech, enoki and shiitake mushrooms, but any combination will do.

3 Add a dash of olive oil, red chilli and the garlic to a large pan.

4 Stir-fry for a minute, add a dash more olive oil and then the mushrooms, stirring constantly for three to four minutes, until cooked.

5 Add some parsley, a dash of white wine and a pinch of salt and cook for a further minute. Serve on top of the grilled slices of polenta and drizzle with a little extra virgin olive oil.

CHEF'S TIP

Don't throw away the stems of your mushrooms - save them for making soups or stocks. You can freeze them for up to six months in an airtight container. Remember to leave half an inch of space for expansion.

PER SERVING

332	7g	16g	2g	34g	3g	0.5g
CALORIES	PROTEIN	FAT	SAT FAT	CARBS	FIBRE	SALT

Minted pea soup

Serve this cool green soup as a starter for a health-conscious dinner party

TOP TIP
Take chilled soups out of the fridge 10 minutes before serving, as they taste better if not too cold.

Serves: 2
Preparation time:
5 minutes
Cooking time:
12 minutes

INGREDIENTS

Sunflower oil
100g onion, chopped
150g potato, peeled and diced
500ml vegetable stock
250g peas
6-10 mint leaves
Salt and pepper
Crème fraîche or
Greek yoghurt
Black pepper, freshly ground

METHOD

1 Add a dash of sunflower oil to a pan on a low heat.

2 Gently soften the onion but don't allow it to brown.

3 Now add the potato and vegetable stock. Simmer for 10 to 12 minutes until the potato is soft, then add the peas and mint leaves.

4 Return to the boil, remove from the heat and blend. Taste and season with salt and pepper.

5 Serve hot or cold with a blob of crème fraîche or Greek yoghurt, some freshly ground black pepper and a sprig of fresh mint.

PER SERVING

282	11g	7.5g	1.5g	29g	10g	0.7g
CALORIES	PROTEIN	FAT	SAT FAT	CARBS	FIBRE	SALT

Cauliflower soup

Boost your immunity with this comforting winter favourite

Serves: 6
Preparation time: 10 minutes
Cooking time: 25 minutes

INGREDIENTS

1 potato, peeled and chopped
1 large onion, peeled and chopped
1 whole cauliflower
750ml chicken or vegetable stock
White pepper and salt
3 tbsp ground almonds
1 tbsp half-fat crème fraîche
Toasted sliced almonds
Chopped chives

METHOD

1 Add the potato to a pan with the onion and cauliflower broken into florets.

2 Add the chicken or vegetable stock, bring to the boil, then turn down the heat, cover and simmer gently for about 25 minutes.

3 Blend thoroughly, taste and season with white pepper and salt, then add the ground almonds and half-fat crème fraîche. Blend again and serve. Garnish with a few toasted, sliced almonds and some chopped chives.

PER SERVING

159	7g	6g	0.8g	11g	4g	0.4g
CALORIES	PROTEIN	FAT	SAT FAT	CARBS	FIBRE	SALT

Quinoa pilaf

Experiment with health-giving wholegrains
to replace pasta or potatoes

Serves: 2
Preparation time:
15 minutes
Cooking time:
15 minutes

INGREDIENTS

60g quinoa
470ml boiling water or hot stock
Olive oil
1 red and 1 yellow pepper,
chopped
1 leek, chopped
25g sunflower seeds
25g pistachio nuts
25g parsley, chopped
5 dried apricots, chopped
1 tsp wholegrain mustard
Juice of ½ a lemon
Salt and pepper

METHOD

1 Add the quinoa to a pan with boiling water or stock, add the lid and simmer for 15 minutes.

2 Meanwhile, in another pan, add a dash of olive oil and throw in the red and yellow peppers and leek, and cook for five minutes until softened.

3 Add a handful of sunflower seeds, a few pistachio nuts, some parsley and dried apricots and turn off the heat when the quinoa is soft. Drain off any excess water and mix the grains with the vegetables.

4 Add a teaspoon of mustard, a dash of olive oil, the lemon juice, more chopped parsley, and season with salt and freshly ground black pepper.

PER SERVING

(369)	(12g)	(20g)	(3g)	(33g)	(7g)	(0.3g)
CALORIES	PROTEIN	FAT	SAT FAT	CARBS	FIBRE	SALT

Did you know?

Quinoa is not only quick to make, with a wonderful nutty taste, it's also high in protein, making it a good choice for vegetarians and vegans.

TOP TIP
Bulgar wheat, couscous and wild rice can be used in this dish to add variety.

Caesar salad

Classic Caesar salads can
be laden with fat and salt,
so try this lighter version

Serves: 4
Preparation time:
10 minutes
Cooking time:
10 minutes

INGREDIENTS

FOR THE SALAD
1 cos lettuce
1 little gem lettuce
20g Parmesan cheese shavings

FOR THE DRESSING
30g Parmesan cheese,
finely grated
2 tbsp live low-fat
organic yoghurt
1 tbsp extra virgin olive oil
1 tsp Dijon mustard
Juice from ¼ of a lemon
1 tsp Worcestershire sauce
A large pinch white pepper

FOR THE CROUTONS
1 dsp olive oil
1 clove garlic, crushed
2 sprigs fresh or 1 tsp
dried rosemary
A little ground black pepper
Half a stale baguette, cubed

METHOD

1 Break the lettuce into individual leaves, wash and thoroughly drain.

2 Mix all the ingredients for the dressing together and leave to infuse.

3 For the croutons, add the olive oil to a bowl with crushed garlic (crush it further with the back of a spoon). Add the rosemary and season with black pepper. Mix well and coat the insides of the bowl with the mixture.

4 Add the bread cubes to the olive oil mixture and toss so the bread is coated with some of the oil and herbs.

5 Spread the cubes onto a baking sheet and bake in a pre-heated oven at 180°C/gas mark 4 for about 10 minutes, turning a couple of times with a spatula and being careful not to burn.

6 To assemble the salad, layer the lettuce in a shallow bowl or plate, saving the smaller leaves until last so you can create concentric circles.

7 Drizzle with the dressing, sprinkle with croutons and top with the shaved Parmesan.

PER SERVING

203	9g	9g	3g	21g	2g	0.9g
CALORIES	PROTEIN	FAT	SAT FAT	CARBS	FIBRE	SALT

Superfood salad

Get maximum nutrients with this simple summer dish

NUTRI TIP
Crunchy salad toppers, pumpkin seeds are rich in plant compounds called phytosterols, which are believed to help lower cholesterol, boost immunity and reduce cancer risk.

Serves: 4
as a starter
Preparation time:
10 minutes

INGREDIENTS

200g mixed leaves
160g marinated
tofu pieces
100g pomegranate seeds
1 tbsp pumpkin seeds
1 orange
Cold-pressed hemp oil

METHOD

1 Add the mixed leaves to a bowl, sprinkle with a pack of the marinated tofu pieces, pomegranate and pumpkin seeds.

2 Add the zest and juice of an orange and a drizzle of the hemp oil.

CHEF'S TIP

Hemp oil is lower in saturated fat than olive oil and contains more beneficial fatty acids.

PER SERVING

144	6.3g	10g	1.3g	7.5g	3g	0.1g
CALORIES	PROTEIN	FAT	SAT FAT	CARBS	FIBRE	SALT

NUTRI TIP
Buy wholemeal wraps when you can. Containing both the bran and the germ of the grain, wholegrain wheat provides more protein, vitamins and minerals than refined white flour, and is rich in phytochemicals and antioxidants.

Falafel wrap

Boost your nutrient intake with this simple, satisfying lunch

Serves: 1
Preparation time: 5 minutes

INGREDIENTS

1 tbsp low-fat cottage cheese
1 wholemeal tortilla
Alfalfa, radish or sunflower sprouts
2-3 crumbled falafels
1 tbsp tahini

METHOD

1 Spread the low-fat cottage cheese onto the tortilla and add a handful of mixed sprouts.

2 Add mixed falafels and drizzle with the tahini. Roll it up and enjoy!

PER SERVING

390	13g	17g	3g	45g	6g	1.4g
CALORIES	PROTEIN	FAT	SAT FAT	CARBS	FIBRE	SALT

CHEF'S TIP

Good health food shops sell a range of sprouted seeds and pulses. Try making houmous with sprouted chickpeas, lemon juice and tahini.

Crispy tofu salad

The perfect vegetarian protein source, tofu is a versatile and nutritious ingredient in savoury dishes

Serves: 2
Preparation time: 10 minutes
Cookery time: 15 minutes

INGREDIENTS

200g firm tofu
4 spring onions
2cm ginger root, freshly grated
½ red chilli, thinly sliced
1 clove of garlic, crushed
1 dsp toasted sesame oil
200g mixed salad leaves
1 tsp sunflower oil
1 dsp soy sauce
1 dsp honey
Juice of ½ a lime

TOP TIP
Try browning strips of tofu drizzled with soy sauce and sesame oil in a pan, and then leave them to absorb the flavours before adding to a stir-fry.

METHOD

1 Cut the block of tofu into 5mm slices and pat dry with kitchen paper.

2 Slice the onions and mix with the ginger, chilli, garlic and sesame oil.

3 Arrange the mixed salad leaves on plates.

4 Add a little sunflower oil to a pan and cook the tofu until crisp on both sides.

5 Remove the tofu from the pan and reserve.

6 Add the spring onion mixture to the pan and cook for a couple of minutes, stirring constantly, then add the tofu back. Stir, and add the soy sauce, honey and lime juice.

7 Spoon on top of the salad leaves and serve.

PER SERVING

94	22g	8g	3g	9.5g	2g	0.9g
CALORIES	PROTEIN	FAT	SAT FAT	CARBS	FIBRE	SALT

Baked avocado

Broaden your avocado recipe repertoire, for a delicious meal that's packed with flavour

Serves: 4 as a starter
Preparation time: 10 minutes
Cooking time: 25 minutes

INGREDIENTS

2 tbsp couscous
Salt and pepper
Dried oregano
100ml water
8-10 sundried tomatoes, pre-soaked
1 tbsp parsley
1 tbsp olive oil
2 avocados
4 slices of mozzarella

METHOD

1 Add the couscous to a bowl with a little salt and pepper, and a sprinkling of dried oregano.

2 Cover with boiling water, put a plate on top of the bowl and set aside for 10 minutes.

3 Meanwhile, shred the sundried tomatoes and chop the parsley.

4 Mix the couscous with the tomato and parsley, and add the olive oil.

5 Halve and peel the avocados, de-stone and add a mound of the couscous to each cavity.

6 Cover with a slice of mozzarella and bake in an oven pre-heated to 180°C/gas mark 4 for 10 to 12 minutes, until the cheese melts and has browned a little.

7 Serve with salad. If you sprinkle the halved avocados with lemon juice, you can prepare them in advance, then just pop in the oven when guests arrive.

PER SERVING

226	4.5g	25g	6g	5.5g	3.5g	0.4g
CALORIES	PROTEIN	FAT	SAT FAT	CARBS	FIBRE	SALT

Red cabbage salad

Use this nutritious and vitamin-packed vegetable to make a colourful salad

TOP TIP
Red cabbage contains the anti-inflammatory amino acid glutamine and the powerful antioxidant anthocyanin, which could help boost your brain power.

Serves: 6
Preparation time:
5 minutes
Cooking time:
10 minutes

INGREDIENTS

400g red cabbage, shredded
100ml boiling water
1 apple, ½ peeled and chopped,
the other ½ chopped with
skin left on
Sea salt and white pepper
2 tbsp walnut pieces
Dash extra virgin olive oil

METHOD

1 Add the finely shredded cabbage to the pan of boiling water and cook on high with the lid on for five minutes.

2 Add the peeled, chopped apple, mix well and cook for a further five minutes, keeping the lid on and making sure there's still a little water in the bottom of the pan, adding another dash if the cabbage sticks.

3 Test the cabbage is cooked but retains a little crunchiness, and drain off excess water (there should be very little as you're aiming to steam the cabbage in its own juices).

4 Add the other half of the chopped apple, a good pinch each of salt and white pepper, two tablespoons of walnut pieces and a dash of olive oil. Mix well and serve.

PER SERVING

70	1g	5g	0.5g	4g	1.7g	0.1g
CALORIES	PROTEIN	FAT	SAT FAT	CARBS	FIBRE	SALT

Pastry-free quiche

Try our waistline-friendly version of this classic dish

Serves: 4
Preparation time:
10 minutes
Cooking time: 15 minutes

INGREDIENTS

250g asparagus
A bunch of spring onions
Olive oil
6 free-range eggs
1 tbsp reduced-fat crème fraîche
Salt and white pepper
A little grated Cheddar
Sunflower oil

METHOD

1 Pre-heat the oven to 180°/gas mark 4. Trim the stalks from the asparagus. Cut the tender spears to 6cm lengths, then chop the rest into 5mm pieces. Trim a bunch of spring onions and cut into 2cm lengths.

2 Add a dash of olive oil and the 5mm pieces of asparagus to a pan and cook for two minutes. Add the 6cm spears, stir for two minutes, then add the spring onions and cook a further two minutes. Cover and turn off the heat.

3 Beat the eggs with the reduced-fat crème fraîche and a generous pinch of salt and white pepper.

4 Brush four 10cm individual flan trays with sunflower oil, divide the veg mixture between them, sprinkle with a little grated Cheddar. Then add the eggs and bake for 10-15 minutes.

CHEF'S TIP

Using strong or mature cheese means you can use less – so you get all the flavour without the fat.

PER SERVING

261	15g	21g	5.5g	3g	2g	0.4g
CALORIES	PROTEIN	FAT	SAT FAT	CARBS	FIBRE	SALT

Butternut squash risotto

A vibrant orange, this is much lower in fat
than a traditional risotto, yet still tastes rich

Serves: 3
Preparation time: 10 minutes
Cooking time: 30 minutes

INGREDIENTS

1 medium butternut squash, cubed
1 large white onion
1-2 garlic cloves
1l vegetable or chicken stock
Dash of olive oil
150g risotto rice

Salt and black pepper
A knob of butter
1 tbsp half-fat crème fraîche
1 tbsp grated Parmesan cheese
Fresh basil to serve

METHOD

1 Halve, peel and de-seed the butternut squash and roughly dice into a mixture of 1 and 2cm cubes. Finely chop the onion and crush one or two cloves of garlic.

2 Put the vegetable or chicken stock into a pan (stock cubes are fine), bring it to a boil, then turn down the heat and keep it simmering gently.

3 With a dash of olive oil in a separate saucepan, add the onion and cook for five minutes over a low-medium heat, until starting to brown. Now add the butternut squash and risotto rice, stirring well.

4 Season with the garlic, a few grinds of pepper and a good pinch of salt.

Stir for two minutes, then add two ladles of stock and stir again.

5 Regularly stir the risotto for 20-25 minutes, adding hot stock a little at a time so the rice is just covered. The risotto should be very gently bubbling. Test the rice to make sure it's cooked 'al dente' (slightly firm), adding any remaining stock if needed.

6 Finally, add the butter, crème fraîche and freshly grated Parmesan cheese. Stir vigorously for one minute, cover and allow to stand for two minutes. Serve with extra Parmesan, black pepper and fresh basil.

CHEF'S TIP

Stirring is essential, the more you stir the creamier the risotto! Keep stock simmering in a separate pan, so it doesn't reduce the temperature and stop the rice cooking. Add a little stock at a time; if you run out, just add boiling water.

PER SERVING

447	9g	9g	3.7g	60g	6g	1.1g
CALORIES	PROTEIN	FAT	SAT FAT	CARBS	FIBRE	SALT

FISH DISHES

Lower in fat but high in taste, these recipes are surprisingly simple to make

Thai prawn curry

Spice up your cooking repertoire with
a mouthwatering, guilt-free curry

Serves: 2
Preparation time: 5 minutes
Cooking time: 15 minutes

INGREDIENTS

1 red pepper, chopped
3 spring onions, chopped
Sunflower oil
1 teaspoon Thai curry paste
2cm ginger root, freshly grated
2 garlic cloves, crushed
200ml reduced-fat coconut milk
Fish sauce
12 baby sweetcorn
150g king prawns, uncooked
Coriander, chopped
Juice of ½ lime

CHEF'S TIP

If you accidentally
make a dish too spicy,
add something
sweet, such as
chopped dried
apricots, or grated
apple, to counter
the heat.

METHOD

1 Add red pepper and onions to a
pan with a dash of sunflower oil
and cook for a few minutes until soft.

2 Next, add Thai curry paste, ginger
root and garlic.

3 Cook for two minutes then add
coconut milk and a good dash
of fish sauce.

4 Bring to a gentle boil, then add
sweetcorn and king prawns.

5 Simmer for three minutes, then
throw in a handful of coriander,
plus lime juice, and serve.

PER SERVING

156	8.5g	11g	5g	5g	2g	1g
CALORIES	PROTEIN	FAT	SAT FAT	CARBS	FIBRE	SALT

Prawn cocktail

Look after your waistline with a healthier take on this classic dish

Serves: 2
Preparation time:
10 minutes

INGREDIENTS

½ tsp ketchup
¼ lemon juice
½ tsp soy sauce
White pepper
1 tbsp live natural yoghurt
1 tsp mayonnaise
200g king prawns, cooked
100g mixed leaves
1 cucumber, sliced thin
2 lemon wedges
1 tsp capers
Smoked paprika

METHOD

1 Make the sauce by adding ketchup, the juice of quarter of a lemon, soy sauce and a good pinch of white pepper to a cup and mix well. Stir in natural yoghurt and mayonnaise.

2 Allowing 100g king prawns per person, add three king prawns to the bottom of two glasses. Add half the mixed leaves to each glass, top with the rest of the prawns and add thinly sliced cucumber.

3 Drizzle the sauce on top, add a wedge of lemon and sprinkle capers and a pinch of smoked paprika onto the top of each glass. Serve.

PER SERVING

123	17g	3g	0.5g	4g	2g	1.9g
CALORIES	PROTEIN	FAT	SAT FAT	CARBS	FIBRE	SALT

✳ Did you know?

Prawns contain vitamin B12, a natural energy booster that helps to reduce stress.

NUTRI TIP
Ditch the mayonnaise
and use mashed
avocado with lemon
juice, a pinch of salt
and cayenne pepper
for your dressing
instead. They are
brilliant metabolism
boosters.

Pad Thai

This quick and versatile dish can be adapted to use whichever vegetables are to hand

Serves: 4
Preparation: 10 minutes
Cooking time: 12 minutes

INGREDIENTS

250g noodles
Oil
2 red onions, cut into wedges
175g baby sweetcorn
3 garlic cloves, chopped
1 small chilli, chopped finely
8 raw jumbo king prawns
200g raw tiger prawns
6 shiitake mushrooms, sliced
150g sugar snap peas
200g beansprouts
2 tsp caster sugar
2 tbsp fish sauce
1 lime
Coriander, chopped
75g peanuts, chopped

METHOD

1 Cook noodles according to the pack instructions (around three to five minutes). Plunge them into cold water, drain and reserve.

2 Add a dash of oil to a large pan or wok over a high heat. Add red onions and stir fry for three minutes, then add sweetcorn, garlic and the chilli. Stir for another two minutes.

3 Add jumbo king prawns and after a minute, add tiger prawns and shiitake mushrooms. Stir for a minute.

4 Add the noodles and sugar snap peas, stir for two minutes, then add beansprouts, caster sugar, fish sauce, juice of a lime and a handful of chopped coriander and stir for a further two minutes.

5 Put into a bowl and top with peanuts.

6 For a side dish, cut half a cucumber into ribbons with a vegetable peeler, then add fresh coriander leaves and a squeeze of lime.

PER SERVING

| 500 | 24g | 15g | 2.5g | 61g | 4g | 1.8g |
| CALORIES | PROTEIN | FAT | SAT FAT | CARBS | FIBRE | SALT |

CHEF'S TIP

Stir-frying is a quick way to cook, so chop and measure all the ingredients before you start cooking.

TOP TIP
To stop fish cakes crumbling in the pan, place them in the fridge for 30 minutes before cooking.

Fish cakes

Trade calories, but not taste, with these delicious omega 3-rich patties

Serves 4
Preparation time: 10 minutes
Cooking time: 30 minutes

INGREDIENTS

Sunflower oil
1 small onion, finely chopped
Dash of dry white wine
100ml milk
2 heaped tsp cornflour
250g organic salmon
200g white fish (hoki or
pollack are sustainable)
Salt
White pepper
400g peeled potatoes, boiled
and mashed
2 heaped tbsp wholemeal flour
2 heaped tsp smoked paprika

FOR THE SAUCE
3 tbsp half-fat crème fraîche
2 tbsp fresh dill, chopped
1 tbsp lemon juice
Grated zest of half an
unwaxed lemon
Salt
White pepper

METHOD

1 Heat a pan and add a dash of sunflower oil. Once the oil is warmed, add the onion and sauté gently for about three to five minutes until softened. As soon as the onions start to brown, add a dash of wine and cook for a minute or two, or until the wine has almost disappeared.

2 Mix a small amount of the milk with the cornflour and set aside. Add the rest of the milk to the onion. Add the salmon and white fish, salt and pepper to the pan, cover and simmer for three to four minutes until the fish is cooked.

3 Remove the fish from the pan, and thicken the sauce by gradually adding the cornflour mixture, stirring all the time. Once thickened to a paste (it's not a sauce), mix well into the mashed potato, then carefully fold in the fish.

4 Mix the flour and paprika on a plate. Wet your hands and form the potato and fish mixture into eight patties, then dredge each with the flour and paprika mixture. You can cook them now, or refrigerate until needed.

5 To cook, add a dash of oil to a hot frying pan and place the fish cakes in it, browning gently for three to four minutes on each side.

6 Combine the ingredients for the sauce and mix well. Serve the sauce and the fish cakes with a large green salad to accompany.

PER SERVING

385 CALORIES	25g PROTEIN	19g FAT	6g SAT FAT	31g CARBS	2g FIBRE	0.7g SALT

Fish pie

Tuck into this lower-calorie version of our favourite winter warmer

Serves: 6
Preparation time: 30 minutes
Cooking time: 30 minutes

INGREDIENTS

1kg celeriac, peeled and cubed
250g salmon
150g undyed smoked haddock
1 sprig fresh dill
500ml milk
2 tbsp cornflower
1 tsp Dijon mustard
75g grated cheese
Black pepper
150g raw king prawns

METHOD

1 Pre-heat oven to 190°C/gas mark 5. Boil the celeriac for 15 minutes, drain well and mash.

2 Meanwhile, add salmon and haddock to a pan with dill and 450ml milk. Simmer gently for eight minutes, but don't boil. Remove the fish from the milk and reserve. Discard the dill.

3 Add cornflour and Dijon mustard to 50ml cold milk and mix well. Heat the milk and gradually stir in the cornflour mixture, stirring constantly until the sauce has thickened. Then, stir in grated cheese and a good sprinkle of black pepper.

4 Remove any skin or bone from the fish and flake it evenly over an ovenproof dish. Scatter raw king prawns on top, then spoon over the sauce. Top with the celeriac and bake in the oven for 25 30 minutes. Sprinkle with chopped dill and serve.

PER SERVING

258	26g	13g	6g	9g	8g	1.4g
CALORIES	PROTEIN	FAT	SAT FAT	CARBS	FIBRE	SALT

CHEF'S TIP

Scrape a fork across the top of the mashed celeriac, so the surface is uneven. This creates little crispy bits on top.

NUTRI TIP
The curing process requires salt, so smoked fish is high in sodium. Use it sparingly in your cooking, to help avoid high blood pressure.

TOP TIP
A fresh crab should smell of the sea; if it has a slight ammonia smell, don't buy it!

Crab linguine

Make the most of an often-neglected seafood with this flavoursome recipe

Serves: 4
Preparation time: 15 minutes
Cooking time: 10-15 minutes

INGREDIENTS

1 onion, chopped finely
1 orange sweet pepper, chopped finely
1 tsp chillies, crushed
2-3 cloves of garlic, crushed
Dried oregano
250g dried linguine
200g mixed crabmeat
Juice of 1 unwaxed lemon
3 tablespoons parsley, chopped
1 teaspoon extra virgin olive oil
Wedge of lemon

METHOD

1 Fry onion in a pan with pepper and chillies.

2 Stir until the onion has softened but not browned.

3 Add garlic and a good pinch of dried oregano.

4 Meanwhile, cook linguine in boiling water and drain.

5 Add crabmeat, lemon juice, and parsley to the pan. Mix, then toss in the hot pasta, stirring well to ensure an even coating.

6 Drizzle with a tablespoon of extra virgin olive oil and serve with a wedge of lemon.

PER SERVING

310	18g	5g	0.7g	48g	4g	0.6g
CALORIES	PROTEIN	FAT	SAT FAT	CARBS	FIBRE	SALT

✳ Did you know?

Crab is a rich source of omega-3 fatty acids, which aid brain function and memory. Studies have shown that they may also help to prevent breast cancer.

Fragrant mackerel

Get a delicate taste of the Orient with this Asian-inspired recipe

Serves: 3
Preparation time: 10 minutes
Cooking time: 25-30 minutes

INGREDIENTS

1 stick lemongrass, crushed
4 slices lime
3cm ginger root, peeled and shredded
6 garlic cloves, lightly crushed and unpeeled
3 mackerel (whole, headless, cleaned)
1 tbsp soy sauce
1 tbsp mirin (Japanese rice condiment)
Juice from ½ lime
½ chilli, deseeded and shredded
Coriander

METHOD

1 Pre-heat oven to 200°C/gas mark 6 . Place a large sheet of foil on a baking tray and scatter with lime, ginger, lemongrass and garlic.

2 Make three slashes on each side of the mackerel and lay them on the foil on top of the lemongrass and other ingredients.

3 Drizzle the fish with soy sauce, mirin and lime juice, then sprinkle shredded chilli on top.

4 Fold the foil and crimp the edges to create a sealed parcel and bake in oven for 25 to 30 minutes.

5 Discard the lemongrass. Drizzle the cooking juices on top and garnish with a little shredded chilli, some fresh lime and coriander.

PER SERVING

(393)	(33g)	(28g)	(6g)	(0g)	(0g)	(1.2g)
CALORIES	PROTEIN	FAT	SAT FAT	CARBS	FIBRE	SALT

Did you know?

Mackerel contains a powerful antioxidant, coenzyme Q-10. It's essential for a healthy immune system and helps prevent the premature ageing of skin cells.

NUTRI TIP
Don't overcook your fish. Cooking until just firm means the flesh holds together and the bones come away easily.

NUTRI TIP
Don't forget to experiment with other types of omega 3-rich oily fish, such as trout, mackerel, sardines and fresh tuna. You should aim to eat oily fish twice a week.

Sesame-crusted salmon

Fish in a flash: this salmon supper shows fast food can be healthy

Serves: 2
Preparation time: 10 minutes
Cooking time: 15 minutes

INGREDIENTS

2 salmon steaks (120g each)
Juice of ½ lemon
2 tbsp sesame seeds
300g stir-fry vegetables
Toasted sesame oil
Sunflower oil
1 dessertspoon soy sauce

METHOD

1 Pre-heated the oven to 180°C/gas mark 4 . Thoroughly coat both salmon steaks with the lemon juice, put on a plate and sprinkle with sesame seeds, making sure they're well coated. Place on a lightly oiled baking sheet, sprinkle any remaining seeds on top and bake for 12 to 15 minutes.

2 While the salmon cooks, add stir-fry vegetables to a wok with a dash of toasted sesame oil and a small dash of sunflower oil and cook for three to five minutes over a high heat, stirring constantly.

3 Place the vegetables on a dish, break the salmon into chunks and arrange on top of the veg, drizzle over with soy sauce and lemon juice and serve.

PER SERVING

505	31g	39g	6g	6g	6g	1g
CALORIES	PROTEIN	FAT	SAT FAT	CARBS	FIBRE	SALT

✳
Did you know?

Salmon is a great source of potassium, which aids the functioning of the heart, muscle tissues, kidneys and the brain.

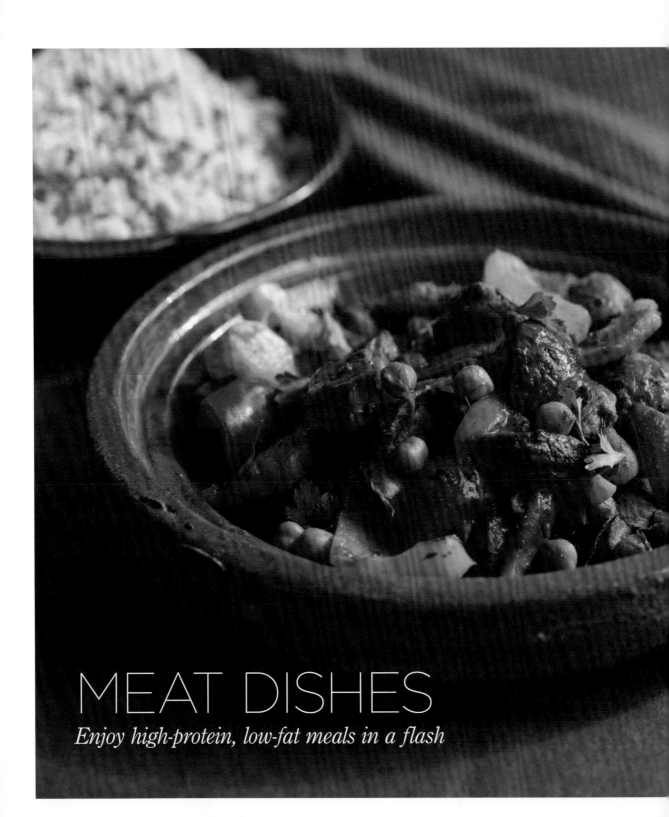

MEAT DISHES

Enjoy high-protein, low-fat meals in a flash

Lamb tagine with lemon couscous

Save time and calories with this delicious adaptation of Morocco's most famous dish

Serves: 4
Preparation time: 10 minutes
Cooking time: 15 minutes

INGREDIENTS

400g lean leg of lamb steaks
Dash of sunflower oil
1 red onion, sliced
1 yellow and 1 red pepper, chopped
3 cloves garlic, crushed
2 tsp cinnamon, 1 tsp turmeric,
1 tsp chilli
1 tsp ground ginger or 2.5cm ginger,
grated
Pinch of salt
1 x 240g can of chickpeas, drained
1 can of chopped tomatoes

FOR THE COUSCOUS
200g dried couscous
2 tsp cumin
A pinch of salt and plenty of white
pepper
50g dried apricots, chopped in
strips
Juice and grated zest of one lemon
1 tbsp extra virgin olive oil
Large handful freshly-chopped
parsley

METHOD

1 Trim excess fat from the lamb and cut into strips. Add the sunflower oil to a pan and add the lamb, then the onion, and stir for two minutes. Add the peppers and cook for another five minutes, stirring regularly.

2 Add the garlic, cinnamon, turmeric, chilli, ginger and salt. Mix well, then add the tomatoes and chickpeas and bring to a gentle boil. Add a lid and simmer gently for 15 minutes, stirring occasionally.

3 Add the couscous, cumin, salt and pepper to a bowl and stir in 250ml of boiling water. Cover with a plate and leave for 10 minutes. Add the apricots, lemon juice and zest, olive oil and parsley, and fork through.

PER SERVING

423	29g	17g	16g	43g	6g	1g
CALORIES	PROTEIN	FAT	SAT FAT	CARBS	FIBRE	SALT

Turkey burgers

These are unprocessed and low fat – they're brilliant for BBQs

Serves: 4
Preparation time: 5 minutes
Cooking time: 5 minutes

INGREDIENTS

4 x 100g free-range turkey breast steaks
Dash of sunflower oil
4 seeded baps, split open
150g mixed salad leaves
1 beefsteak tomato, sliced
4 small pinches of salt and pepper
1 small red onion, sliced

METHOD

1 Brush the turkey with a little oil and place on the barbecue for one minute then turn 90° degrees and cook for another minute and a half. This gives a criss-cross effect. Turn the turkey over and repeat on the other side.

2 When the turkey is nearly cooked, open out the baps and toast the inside for 30 seconds on the barbecue.

3 Add the salad leaves and tomato slices, season with salt and pepper, place the turkey on top, add the sliced onions and enjoy!

PER SERVING

| 331 | 33g | 8g | 1.5g | 32g | 6.5g | 1g |
| CALORIES | PROTEIN | FAT | SAT FAT | CARBS | FIBRE | SALT |

Did you know?

Eating turkey can help you to sleep. It contains tryptophan, an essential amino acid that helps the body release the calming chemical, serotonin.

NUTRI TIP
Use free-range turkey steaks. They cook easily and quickly, and they are an excellent source of low-fat protein. They're also high in selenium and B vitamins.

TOP TIP
If you can't resist spicy food, add one chopped chilli and a little grated ginger to the pan at the same time as the onions.

Chicken korma

Craving spice? Try this creamy curry – it's really good for you

Serves: 2
Preparation time: 10 minutes
Cook time: 15–20 minutes

INGREDIENTS

6 tbsp natural yoghurt
1 heaped tsp turmeric
1 tsp ground cumin
1 tsp ground cinnamon
1 tsp ground coriander
Good pinch white pepper
2-3cm peeled and finely
grated fresh ginger
4 cloves garlic, crushed
2 skinless free-range chicken
breast, cubed (350g approx)
Dash of sunflower oil
1 medium onion, finely chopped
200ml vegetable or chicken
stock
2-3 tbsp ground almonds
1 tbsp flaked toasted almonds
Fresh coriander to garnish

METHOD

1 Add two tablespoons of yoghurt to a bowl with the turmeric, cumin, cinnamon, coriander, pepper, ginger and garlic, mix well and leave to stand for a couple of minutes to infuse.

2 Stir the yoghurt mixture again, add the chicken, making sure it is well coated, then set aside.

3 Add the oil to a pan and cook the onion until soft and starting to brown, about five minutes.

4 Add the chicken and marinade to the pan and stir constantly for another five minutes. As soon as it starts to stick, add the stock, mix well and bring to a gentle simmer, add a lid and cook for another five to seven minutes, stirring occasionally.

5 Mix in the ground almonds and allow to cook for a further minute or two, stirring.

6 Remove from the heat, stir in the remaining yoghurt and serve with a sprinkling of toasted almonds, a little fresh coriander and some side dishes, such as mango chutney and chopped red onion and chillies.

PER SERVING

445	20g	20g	3g	9g	1g	0.6g
CALORIES	PROTEIN	FAT	SAT FAT	CARBS	FIBRE	SALT

CHEF'S TIP

Turkey can be used as an alternative in this recipe. It's just as tasty, and lower in fat.

Chicken soup

This healing broth is packed with extra spices –
it's great for fighting winter colds and flu

Serves: 4
Preparation time: 10 minutes
Cooking time: 30 minutes

INGREDIENTS

1 white onion
Dash of vegetable oil
1 stick celery
1 carrot
1 red pepper
1 leek
1 small red chilli
2cm fresh ginger
4-6 garlic cloves
1 skinless chicken breast
1 tbsp pearl barley
1 heaped tsp ground tumeric
2 organic chicken stock cubes
1 litre boiling water
Dash of soy sauce

METHOD

1 Chop the onion finely and add to a pan with a dash of vegetable oil, then cook gently for five minutes, stirring regularly.

2 Chop the stick of celery, a carrot, a red pepper and a leek; finely chop the small red chilli, 2cm fresh ginger root and crush four to six cloves of garlic, then add them all to the pan.

3 Slice the chicken breast into pieces and add it to the pan.

4 Now add the pearl barley, turmeric, stock cubes and boiling water. Mix well, bring to the boil, turn down the heat, add a lid and simmer gently for 25 minutes.

5 Add a dash of soy sauce and serve with a sprig of fresh herbs.

PER SERVING

124	11g	4g	10g	3g	2.2g	0.6g
CALORIES	PROTEIN	FAT	CARBS	FIBRE	SALT	SAT FAT

CHEF'S TIP

For a veggie alternative, use vegetable stock and marinated tofu instead of chicken.

TOP TIP
Let the soup simmer, not boil, in the final stages. This will stop the chicken from becoming too tough.

Southern-style chicken

Satisfy your fast-food craving with this healthy and delicious baked alternative

Serves: 4
Preparation time: 10 minutes
Cooking time: 30 minutes

INGREDIENTS

1 tbsp wholemeal flour
2 heaped tsp paprika
1 heaped tsp turmeric
1 heaped tsp mixed spice
1 heaped tsp ground cumin
1 heaped tsp ground ginger
1 heaped tsp dried thyme
Good pinch of salt
800g free-range chicken drumstick
and thigh portions
2 tbsp lemon juice

CHEF'S TIP

Whole chicken costs less than jointed, so you could joint it yourself, freeze some and make stock with the bones to get the best value and flavour.

✳

To give a tandoori flavour to your chicken, just add a heaped teaspoon of curry powder. Or for a Chinese twist, add one heaped teaspoon of five spice to the spice mixture before coating the chicken.

METHOD

1 Mix the flour, paprika, turmeric, mixed spice, cumin, ginger, thyme and salt together, making sure they're mixed well and with no lumps.

2 Add the chicken to a bowl with the lemon juice and mix well so the meat is completely coated.

3 Toss the chicken in the spice mixture and make sure it's well covered.

4 Lay out the pieces on a lightly oiled baking sheet, skin-side up and sprinkle any leftover spice mixture on top.

5 Roast in a pre-heated oven at 200°C/gas mark 6. After 10 minutes, turn the pieces over and turn again after another 10 minutes, cooking for 25 to 30 minutes in total.

PER SERVING

253	43g	8g	2g	2g	0.5g	0.9g
CALORIES	PROTEIN	FAT	SAT FAT	CARBS	FIBRE	SALT

Burgers

Follow this recipe for a lean and guilt-free burger

Makes: 4 burgers
Prep time: 5 minutes, plus 20 in the fridge
Cooking time: 8 minutes

INGREDIENTS

1 slice wholemeal bread
Good pinch salt
Good pinch white pepper
1–2 cloves crushed garlic (optional)
1 medium free-range egg
250g extra lean steak mince
50g carrot, finely grated
50g onion, finely grated

4 wholemeal buns, sliced in half
1 red onion, thinly sliced
2 tomatoes, sliced
1 little gem lettuce

METHOD

1 Break the bread into a bowl with the salt, pepper and garlic. Add the egg, mix, allow to soak for a couple of minutes, then mix again.

2 Add the minced beef, carrot and onion. Mix well and divide the mixture into four.

3 Wet your hands and shape each portion into a round ball, then flatten it to about 2½cm thick into a burger shape. Cover and place in the fridge for at least 20 minutes.

4 Heat a griddle pan or BBQ, add the burger and leave to cook for three to four minutes. Then flip with a spatula and cook for another three to four minutes (turning a burger too soon may make it crumble).

5 Put the burger on one half of a wholemeal bun, top with slices of onion, tomato, and two or three lettuce leaves, and serve.

PER SERVING

400	25g	15g	4g	34g	8g	1.2g
CALORIES	PROTEIN	FAT	SAT FAT	CARBS	FIBRE	SALT

CHEF'S TIP

Add a teaspoon of herbs or spices, such as dried oregano, mint or chilli flakes. Try curry powder or Chinese five spice for a more exotic taste.

TOP TIP
Avoid pressing the burgers with a spatula while they are cooking; you will reduce the juiciness and flavour. Make holes with a fork instead.

TOP TIP
When loading and rolling your tortilla, don't forget to fold one end in as you roll it up so the filling doesn't drip out.

Chicken and sweet pepper fajitas

This tweaked and tasty Mexican favourite now packs a healthy punch

Makes: 8
Preparation time: 15 minutes
Cook time: 12 minutes

INGREDIENTS

2 boneless, skinless free-range
chicken breasts, cut into strips
(350g-400g approx)
½ tsp paprika
1 tbsp sunflower oil
1-2 red onions, cut into wedges
1 red and 1 yellow pepper,
cut into strips
1 courgette, cut into strips
1 heaped tsp ground cumin
1 heaped tsp oregano
1 tsp chilli flakes (heaped if you
like it hot)
Good pinch of salt
2-3 tbsp water
8 wholemeal tortillas

FOR THE SALSA
3–4 ripe tomatoes, chopped
1 large handful fresh coriander,
roughly chopped
Grated zest and juice of a lime

FOR THE SOURED YOGHURT
4 heaped tbsp live Greek yoghurt
1 tbsp lemon juice

TO SERVE
Shredded lettuce or mixed
leaves

METHOD

1 Make the salsa and soured yoghurt, shred the lettuce and put to one side.

2 Mix the chicken with the paprika, add oil to a pan, add the chicken and cook for two minutes.

3 Add the onion, peppers and courgette and stir for another two minutes.

4 Add the cumin, oregano, chilli flakes and salt and carry on cooking for four to five minutes, stirring regularly.

5 Add the water to the pan, mix well and cover, then turn the heat down really low to keep it hot, adding a little more water if it starts sticking to the pan.

6 Meanwhile, warm the tortillas in a dry frying pan over a medium-low heat. Add the whole stack and turn them regularly, so each one gets a little time in contact with the hot pan.

7 Serve everything together and start building your fajitas.

PER SERVING

276	17g	7g	2.5g	34g	4g	1.2g
CALORIES	PROTEIN	FAT	SAT FAT	CARBS	FIBRE	SALT

CHEF'S TIP

If you have any leftover tortillas, they make excellent, super-crispy thin bases for a homemade pizza.

DESSERTS
Enjoy your favourite post-dinner treats without the guilt

Lemon tart

Serve this zesty dessert as a
waistline-friendly final course

Serves: 8
Preparation time: 30 minutes
Cooking time: 10 minutes +
30–35 minutes

INGREDIENTS

FOR THE PASTRY
150g spelt flour
75g plain flour
Pinch of baking powder
Grated zest of 1 lemon
100ml sunflower oil
75ml water
Pinch of salt

FOR THE FILLING
1 whole free-range egg
and 2 egg yolks
150g caster sugar
Grated zest of 4 unwaxed
lemons, plus
juice of 2 lemons
1 tsp vanilla extract
200g half-fat crème fraîche
250g virtually fat-free quark
(low-fat cream cheese)
Icing sugar to serve

METHOD

1 Mix all the pastry ingredients together,
and roll into a ball. Cover and refrigerate
for 30 minutes.

2 Pre-heat the oven to 180°C/gas mark 4 and
place a baking sheet inside. Roll the pastry to
half a centimetre thick, sprinkling with plenty of
flour, and use it to line a lightly oiled 20cm flan
tin, leaving the edges overlapping the sides (you
can trim these off once the tart is cooked).

3 Place baking paper on top and add some
baking beans (or dried beans or lentils). Place
the tin on the hot baking sheet and bake 'blind'
for 10 minutes. Remove from the oven and turn
the heat down to 160°C/gas mark 3.

4 Meanwhile, beat the egg and egg yolks with
the sugar. Mix the lemon juice, zest, vanilla
extract, crème fraîche and quark, then gradually
stir in the egg and sugar mixture.

5 Remove the paper and beans from the case,
fill with the lemon mixture and bake for 30
to 35 minutes, checking and turning regularly.
Allow to rest for 10 minutes, then trim the edges.
Dust with icing sugar to serve.

TOP TIP
You can replace
the lemons in
this recipe with
oranges or
limes.

PER SERVING

 (334) CALORIES
 (8g) PROTEIN
 (15g) FAT
 (4g) SAT FAT
 (40g) CARBS
 (1g) FIBRE
 (20g) SUGAR

Mango sorbet

Swap ice cream for a healthier frozen dessert

Serves: 8
Preparation time: 10 minutes
Freezing time: 3-4 hours

INGREDIENTS

100g sugar
150ml water
2 ripe mangoes
1 pinch of salt
Juice of 1 lemon juice
Lime zest to serve

METHOD

1 Make a sugar syrup by dissolving the sugar in 150ml of boiling water, then allow to cool a little.

2 Peel two ripe mangoes, remove the flesh from the stones and blend until smooth. Add a pinch of salt and the juice of a lemon, then stir in the syrup, mixing well.

3 Add the mixture to a freezer-proof plastic container so that it's no more than 3-4cm deep. Place in the freezer.

4 After about an hour, it should start freezing around the edges. Mix thoroughly with a fork, bringing the icier edges toward the middle, then return to the freezer for another hour. Mix again, then freeze for another 30-40 minutes and give it a final mix. Freeze for another hour.

5 The sorbet will keep in the freezer for a month. Before serving, remove from the freezer and put in the fridge for 20-30 minutes to soften. Sprinkle with some grated lime zest to serve.

PER SERVING

95	0g	0g	0g	17g	1g	17g
CALORIES	PROTEIN	FAT	SAT FAT	CARBS	FIBRE	SUGAR

Try it!

Mangoes are crammed with vitamins A and C, which are good for unblocking pores and giving you clear skin.

TOP TIP
For ice cream in a flash, freeze two sliced bananas. Once frozen, whizz the banana pieces in a blender. It's great topped with chopped nuts.

Trifle

This classic dessert needn't be fattening. Here yoghurt and crème fraîche replaces cream and custard

Serves: 6
Preparation time: 20 minutes
Cooking time: 15 minutes

INGREDIENTS

FOR THE SPONGE
2 tbsp (75g) self-raising flour
1 tbsp (30g) caster sugar
1 large egg
2 tbsp sunflower oil
2 tbsp milk
1 tsp almond essence
150g raspberries

FOR THE VANILLA YOGHURT
1 tbsp runny honey
200g 0% fat Greek yoghurt
2 tsp natural vanilla extract
3 ripe nectarines or peaches, peeled and sliced
300g strawberries, sliced
200g half-fat crème fraîche
1 tbsp toasted almonds

PER SERVING

(288) CALORIES (11g) PROTEIN (12g) FAT (4g) SAT FAT (32g) CARBS (11g) FIBRE (29g) SUGAR

METHOD

FOR THE SPONGE

1 Pre-heat the oven to 180°C/gas mark 4. Mix the flour and caster sugar. Separate the egg, and beat the whites until fluffy.

2 Add the oil, milk, egg yolk and almond essence together. Mix well, then blend in the flour and sugar.

3 Fold in the egg whites and mix in the raspberries.

4 Add to a lightly oiled cake tin, spreading the mixture out to 1-2cm high, and bake in the oven for 10-15 minutes. Allow to cool.

FOR THE VANILLA YOGHURT

1 Add the honey to 200g of fat-free Greek yoghurt and the vanilla extract. Leave to infuse in the fridge for 10 minutes.

2 Add a piece of sponge to the bottom of six wine glasses and add a layer of peaches. Spoon on the Greek yoghurt, add a layer of strawberries then the crème fraîche. Top with toasted almonds.

Cherry fool

Brimming with health-giving nutrients, cherries add colour and intensity to your dessert

TOP TIP
If using dried cherries, you can plump them up by leaving them to stand in a covered bowl of hot water for 30 minutes.

Serves: 4
Preparation time: 15 minutes
Cooking time: 3 minutes

300g cherries
4 tsp sugar
Lemon juice
2 tbsp water
4 tbsp fat-free live yoghurt
2 tbsp half-fat crème fraîche

METHOD

1 Cut the cherries in half and remove the stones.

2 Add half the cherries to a pan with sugar, a squeeze of lemon juice and water.

3 Add a lid, bring to the boil, then remove from the heat and cool.

4 Meanwhile, mix the yoghurt with the crème fraîche.

5 Mix the raw cherries with the cooked, then add a spoonful to the bottom of two glasses and add alternate layers of the yoghurt mixture and cherries, ending with the cherry mixture.

6 Just before serving, carefully stir the mixture just enough to create swirls of colour without blending everything together.

PER SERVING

299	6g	4g	2.5g	56g	2.5g	56g
CALORIES	PROTEIN	FAT	SAT FAT	CARBS	FIBRE	SUGAR

Blueberry pancakes

You don't have to save these for Shrove Tuesday

Makes: 10 pancakes
Preparation time: 5 minutes
Cooking time: 10-15 minutes

INGREDIENTS

50g butter, melted
1 tbsp caster sugar
200g self-raising flower
Soda bicarbonate
Salt
1 egg, beaten
250ml milk
1 tsp vanilla essence
200g blueberries

CHEF'S TIP

If using frozen blueberries, don't defrost them. This will help them retain their juiciness.

METHOD

1 Add the melted butter to a bowl and mix in the caster sugar, self-raising flour, a pinch of bicarbonate of soda and salt, egg, milk and vanilla essence.

2 Mix to a smooth batter, then stir in the blueberries.

3 Add two tablespoons of the mixture to a pan with a little oil in it and cook on a medium heat for two to three minutes on each side.

4 Serve with a drizzle of maple syrup.

PER SERVING

146	4g	6g	3g	20g	1g	10g
CALORIES	PROTEIN	FAT	SAT FAT	CARBS	FIBRE	SUGAR

Did you know?

Anthocyanins, the pigments in blueberries, prevent the loss of fat in the brain, slowing age-related mental decline.

TOP TIP
To keep pancakes warm, put a plate onto a saucepan of gently simmering water, add the pancakes and cover with another plate.

TOP TIP
You can wrap and keep ginger in the freezer for up to two months. It's also much easier to grate when frozen.

Ginger cake

Enjoy a slice of cake with afternoon tea – without the guilt!

Makes: 10 slices
Preparation time: 15 minutes
Cooking time: 40 minutes

INGREDIENTS

200g wholemeal flour
1 tsp baking powder
3 tsp ground ginger
2 free-range eggs
100ml sunflower oil
2 tsp vanilla extract
2 tbsp black treacle
2 tbsp blackstrap molasses
75g (about four or five pieces) stem ginger in syrup, chopped
1 dsp syrup from the ginger

METHOD

1 Pre-heat the oven to 175˚C/gas mark 4. Mix the flour, baking powder and ground ginger together and shake through a sieve. You will end up with the wheat bran left in the sieve, so add this back to the rest of the flour.

2 Separate the eggs and whisk the whites until thick.

3 In another bowl, add the egg yolks, oil, vanilla, treacle and molasses, and beat until well mixed.

4 Now stir the flour into the molasses mixture, add half the chopped ginger and gently fold in the egg whites.

5 Put the mixture into a lightly-oiled loaf tin (approximately 17x11cm), sprinkling the rest of the ginger on top.

6 Cover with foil and place the loaf tin in another, larger baking tray, adding water so it comes halfway up the tin. Bake for 35 to 40 minutes.

7 Allow to cool a little in the tin, then turn out onto a plate and drizzle the ginger syrup over the top.

PER SERVING

(185) CALORIES	(4g) PROTEIN	(9g) FAT	(1.5g) SAT FAT	(22g) CARBS	(2.5g) FIBRE	(10g) SUGAR

✳ Did you know?

Ginger aids digestion and has been proven to reduce the symptoms of motion sickness.

Apple charlotte

Serve this pudding instead of calorific apple pie, with a dollop of low-fat natural yoghurt

Serves: 4
Preparation time: 10 minutes
Cooking time: 20 minutes

INGREDIENTS

**3 apples, peeled, cored
and chopped
200ml apple juice
2 tbsp molasses sugar
2 tsp cinnamon
Dash of sunflower oil
4-5 slices of wholemeal bread,
crusts removed
1 egg yolk
75g raspberries**

METHOD

1 Pre-heat the oven to 180˚C/gas mark 4. Add the apples to a saucepan with 100ml of the apple juice and simmer until soft. Remove the apples from the pan, leaving the juice behind. Place in a bowl and mash with a fork.

2 Add the sugar and cinnamon to the pan with the other 100ml of apple juice and gently dissolve, adding a little more juice if needed. Allow to cool a little. You should end up with around 100ml of syrup. Don't worry about a few lumps, they will bake out.

3 Rub the sunflower oil around a small ovenproof dish. Dip the bread slices in the sugar mixture and use to line the basin.

4 Mix the egg yolk into the apple, put half the mixture in the bread-lined bowl, add the raspberries and top with the remaining apple.

5 Finally, top with more syrup-soaked bread, and spoon on any remaining liquid. Bake for 20 minutes in the pre-heated oven. Check after 15 minutes. If the top is very brown at the edges and cooking too quickly, place a piece of foil on top for the last five minutes.

6 Allow to stand for a few minutes, loosen the edges with a knife and carefully turn out onto a serving plate.

PER SERVING

213 CALORIES	5g PROTEIN	3g FAT	1g SAT FAT	40g CARBS	5.8g FIBRE	26g SUGAR

CHEF'S TIP

Apples will keep for weeks in the salad drawer of the fridge. If you buy a big bag, put some in the fruit bowl and refrigerate the rest.

TOP TIP
Before cooking or eating, gently scrub non-organic apples in cold water, to remove any wax and remaining pesticides.

TOP TIP
Vanilla brings out a smooth flavour in chocolate. If your chocolate is not the best quality, add a drop of vanilla essence while it's melting.

Chocolate mousse

No need to feel guilty with this low-fat version of the sumptuous dessert

Serves: 4
Preparation time: 10 minutes
Chill time: 15 minutes–24 hours

INGREDIENTS

**100g chocolate bar with
85 per cent cocoa solids, plus
a few squares to serve
20g caster sugar
200ml half-fat crème fraîche
2 free-range egg whites
4 raspberries, to serve**

METHOD

1 Place a bowl over a saucepan of gently simmering water. Break the chocolate into squares and add to the bowl, making sure the bowl is not touching the water. Add the sugar and gently stir until the chocolate melts and the sugar dissolves.

2 Mix in half the crème fraîche, then remove the bowl from the saucepan and stir in the rest of the crème fraîche.

3 Add the egg whites to another bowl and whisk until fluffy, then fold them carefully into the chocolate.

4 Spoon into four glasses or espresso cups and refrigerate for at least 15 minutes before serving.

5 Garnish with some grated chocolate and a raspberry – and they're ready to enjoy.

PER SERVING

226	3g	13g	8.5g	20g	0.5g	20g
CALORIES	PROTEIN	FAT	SAT FAT	CARBS	FIBRE	SUGAR

Did you know?
Chocolate contains flavonoids, antioxidants that reduce the risk of heart failure by increasing the flexibility of veins and arteries.

Sticky toffee pudding

Make this decadent dessert a little easier on your conscience

Serves: 10
Preparation time: 15 minutes
Cooking time: 25–30 minutes

INGREDIENTS

200g dried dates, stoned
150g wholemeal self-raising flour
½ tsp ground mixed spice
½ tsp ground ginger
1 level tsp bicarbonate of soda
2 large free-range eggs
3 tbsp natural yoghurt
75ml sunflower oil
100g caster sugar

FOR THE TOFFEE SAUCE
60g unsalted butter
75g dark unrefined muscovado sugar
150ml half-fat crème fraîche
1 tbsp of blended dates

METHOD

1 Pre-heat your oven to 180°C/gas mark 4. Put the dates in a bowl and cover with boiling water for two minutes, then drain and blend into a paste (reserving one tablespoon of the paste for the sauce).

2 Mix the flour, mixed spice, ginger and bicarbonate of soda together and shake through a sieve. Some bits of the wholegrain flour won't go through the sieve, but just add these into the bowl after – you're trying to get air into the flour but not removing the bran.

3 In another bowl, beat together the eggs, yoghurt, oil, caster sugar and dates, then fold in the flour.

4 Put the mixture into a lightly oiled dish and bake for 25 to 30 minutes.

5 For the toffee sauce, add the butter, sugar, crème fraîche and blended dates to a pan, stirring over a low heat until the sugar dissolves.

6 Just before serving, pour the hot sauce over the pudding.

PER SERVING

(311) CALORIES	(5g) PROTEIN	(15g) FAT	(6g) SAT FAT	(40g) CARBS	(3g) FIBRE	(32g) SUGAR

CHEF'S TIP

For a popular dinner party pudding that can be prepared in advance, make this in individual ramekins and reduce the cooking time to 15 minutes.

TOP TIP
Rinse dates and other dried fruits to reduce their stickiness when chopping them or using a food processor.

SNACK RECIPES

These delicious healthy treats will stave off hunger and unhealthy snacking. They'll help keep you looking slim and toned, too

TOP TIP
Guacamole is another healthy dip, thanks to the monounsaturated and polyunsaturated fats, plus vitamins and minerals in its avocados. Half a medium avocado counts as one of your five-a-day and contains 138 calories and 14.1g fat.

Delicious dips

Add a twist to houmous, and serve it with crudités for a quick, nutritious party dip

Serves: 8
Preparation time: 10 minutes
Cooking time: 30 minutes

Beetroot & horseradish houmous

INGREDIENTS

2 beetroot
1 tbsp horseradish sauce
300g pot of houmous

METHOD

1 Peel and quarter the fresh beetroot and roast for 30 minutes in a hot oven, or use two pre-cooked beetroot (not in vinegar).

2 Add to a bowl with horseradish sauce and houmous, blend well and serve.

PER SERVING

155 CALORIES	6g PROTEIN	10g FAT	1g SAT FAT
11g CARBS	3g FIBRE	1.4g SALT	

Curried houmous with mango chutney

INGREDIENTS

1 tbsp medium curry paste
1 tbsp mango chutney
300g pot of houmous

METHOD

1 Stir the curry paste and chutney into the houmous.

PER SERVING

156 CALORIES	6g PROTEIN	10g FAT	1g SAT FAT
10g CARBS	2.5g FIBRE	1.5g SALT	

Sesame houmous

INGREDIENTS

1 tbsp tahini
1 tbsp sesame seeds
300g pot of houmous

METHOD

1 Stir the tahini and sesame seeds into the houmous.

PER SERVING

185 CALORIES	7g PROTEIN	14g FAT	2g SAT FAT
8g CARBS	3g FIBRE	1.3g SALT	

Healthy popcorn

Popcorn is low in fat and good source of fibre, plus it's quick and fun to make and can be flavoured in many ways

Serves: 4
Preparation time: 3 minutes
Cooking time: 3-5 minutes

Basic popcorn

INGREDIENTS

2 tbsp (30g) popping corn

METHOD

1 Add popping corn to a large hot pan over a medium heat, and place the lid on.

2 After a minute or so, you'll hear the corn start popping. Cook for a further two to three minutes, shaking the pan several times.

3 Remove from the heat and leave for one minute to make sure the corn has stopped popping. Remove any un-popped kernels, and it's ready to eat or add flavourings (see right).

PER SERVING

(42) CALORIES (1g) PROTEIN (2g) FAT (0.2g) SAT FAT

(6g) CARBS (0.5g) FIBRE (0.1g) SALT

Cheesy garlic & thyme popcorn

INGREDIENTS

15-20g butter
2-3 cloves garlic, crushed
2 tsp fresh thyme, chopped
Salt and pepper
1 litre popped corn
1 tbsp Parmesan, finely grated

METHOD

1 Add butter to a pan with garlic, thyme and a pinch of salt and pepper.

2 Cook gently for two minutes, without browning the garlic.

3 Add popped corn and Parmesan. Mix well and serve.

PER SERVING

(86) CALORIES (2g) PROTEIN (4.5g) FAT (3g) SAT FAT

(5.5g) CARBS (0.5g) FIBRE (0.1g) SALT

Chilli lemon popcorn

INGREDIENTS

1 tbsp olive oil
1 red chilli, finely chopped
1 tsp smoked paprika
1 unwaxed lemon
1 litre popped corn

METHOD

1 Add olive oil to a pan with red chilli and smoked paprika. Cook gently until the paprika dissolves.

2 Add the juice and grated zest of an unwaxed lemon and heat until the juice has almost evaporated.

3 Mix in popped corn and serve.

PER SERVING

(67) CALORIES (1g) PROTEIN (4.5g) FAT (0.5g) SAT FAT

(5.5g) CARBS (0.5g) FIBRE (0.1g) SALT

Honey, oat & spelt cookies

Indulge your sweet-tooth cravings with this low-fat comfort food

Makes: 16 cookies
Preparation time: 20 minutes
Cooking time: 10 minutes

INGREDIENTS

DRY INGREDIENTS
125g rolled oats
100g wholegrain spelt flour
½ tsp bicarbonate soda
Pinch salt
2 heaped tsp cinnamon
½ tsp ground ginger
100g raisins

WET INGREDIENTS
6 tbsp runny honey
100ml oil
1 egg (beaten with 1 tbsp water)
1 tsp vanilla extract

TO SPRINKLE
½ tsp ground cinnamon, mixed
with ½ tsp caster sugar

TOP TIP
This basic mixture can be used to make a variety of biscuits. Jazz them up with other dried fruit, spices, nuts and seeds. Try coconut oil for a nutty flavour.

PER COOKIE

| 131 CALORIES | 3g PROTEIN | 6g FAT | 0.7g SAT FAT | 17g CARBS | 1.5g FIBRE | 8.5g SUGAR |

METHOD

1 Pre-heat the oven to 160°C/gas mark 3. Meanwhile, mix all the dry ingredients together in a large bowl.

2 Mix all the wet ingredients together in another bowl.

3 Stir the dry ingredients into the wet, then chill for 10 minutes in the fridge.

4 Drop small spoonfuls onto two greased baking sheets, leaving plenty of space between them, as they spread out. Press down with a fork to ensure even cooking.

5 Bake for about 10 minutes, or until golden on the bottom.

6 Allow them to cool, then sprinkle with a little of the sugar and cinnamon mixture.

Banana bread

Low in fat and sweetened only with dried fruit, this is far healthier than a pastry or cake

Serves: 10
Preparation time: 10 minutes
Cooking time: 55 minutes

INGREDIENTS

4 ripe bananas
1 egg
100ml sunflower oil
2 tsp mixed spice
100g raisins
100g dates, chopped
150g wholemeal flour
1 tsp baking powder
1 tbsp sunflower seeds

METHOD

1 Add bananas, egg, sunflower oil, mixed spice, raisins and dates to a food processor and blend until smooth.

2 Add mix to a bowl and stir in wholemeal flour and baking powder.

3 Pour the mixture into a large (900g) lightly oiled loaf tin and sprinkle the top with a tablespoon of sunflower seeds.

4 Bake in a preheated oven at 180ºC/gas mark 4 for 15 minutes. Place some foil on top and bake for a further 30-40 minutes.

PER SERVING

200	4g	9g	1g	27g	3g	18g
CALORIES	PROTEIN	FAT	SAT FAT	CARBS	FIBRE	SUGAR

TOP TIP
To make carrot cake muffins without the fattening icing, try substituting the apple and cranberries for carrot and spices, such as cinnamon, nutmeg and cloves.

Cranberry and almond muffins

For a delicious breakfast on the go, try this sweet treat

Serves: 8
Preparation time: 10 minutes
Cooking time: 15–20 minutes

INGREDIENTS

100ml sunflower oil
1 tbsp caster sugar
2 eggs
2 tbsp low-fat yoghurt
1 apple, unpeeled and grated
100g dried cranberries
125g wholemeal flour
50g porridge oats
1 tbsp flaked almonds
1½ tsp baking powder
Sugar

METHOD

1 Pre-heat the oven to 180°C/gas mark 4. Add sunflower oil to a bowl with caster sugar, eggs, yoghurt and apple, then beat.

2 In another bowl, mix together cranberries, flour, porridge oats, almonds and baking powder.

3 Gently fold the dry mixture into the wet mixture but don't over mix. Spoon into eight paper muffin cases in a muffin tin, sprinkle a few more sliced almonds on top and bake for 15 to 20 minutes. Garnish with a sprinkle of sugar and a few more cranberries, then serve.

PER SERVING

253 CALORIES	5g PROTEIN	16g FAT	2g SAT FAT	29g CARBS	3.5g FIBRE	16g SUGAR

Granola

This tasty breakfast is low in fat and has no refined sugar

Serves: 6
Preparation time: 5 minutes
Cooking time: 25-30 minutes

INGREDIENTS

150g rolled oats
30g flaked almonds
30g pumpkin seeds
30g sunflower seeds
1 tbsp honey
1 dsp blackstrap molasses
1 tsp ground cinnamon
50g raisins
50g apricots, chopped

METHOD

1 Preheat the oven at 150°C/gas mark 2. Mix the oats with the almonds, pumpkin seeds and sunflower seeds, and reserve.

2 Add honey, molasses and cinnamon to a large pan. Gently warm until the cinnamon has dissolved and the mix is runny. Then stir in the oat mixture until it's well coated.

3 Lightly oil a baking sheet, spread the mixture over it and bake for 15 minutes.

4 Remove from the oven and add the raisins and apricots. Mix well, spread over the baking sheet and return to the oven for another 10 minutes. Allow to cool before storing. Keeps for up to two weeks in an airtight container.

PER SERVING

225 CALORIES | 7g PROTEIN | 10g FAT | 0.9g SAT FAT | 28g CARBS | 3.5g FIBRE | 9g SUGAR

Berry smoothie

This nutritious, protein-rich drink
will set you up for the day ahead

Serves: 1
Preparation time: 5 minutes

INGREDIENTS

80g frozen raspberries
80g frozen blueberries
200ml oat milk
2 tbsp live natural yoghurt
100g silken tofu
1 tbsp runny honey

METHOD

1 Add the raspberries, blueberries, oat
milk, yoghurt, tofu and runny honey
to a jug and blend until smooth.

PER SERVING

(336)	(16g)	(10g)	(4.5g)	(44g)	(5g)	(36g)
CALORIES	PROTEIN	FAT	SAT FAT	CARBS	FIBRE	SUGAR

TOP TIP
If you don't want to use
tofu, whey or hemp
protein powders are a
good substitute. Use
just one scoop (30g)
in this recipe.

Pomegranate & coconut water

Rehydrate naturally with this tangy après-sports juice

Serves: 1
Preparation time: 5 minutes

INGREDIENTS

300ml coconut water
100ml pomegranate juice
Juice of half a lime
A small pinch of salt

METHOD

1 Mix everything together, making sure the salt is completely dissolved.

PER SERVING

118	2g	1g	0.6g	25g	5g	25g
CALORIES	PROTEIN	FAT	SAT FAT	CARBS	FIBRE	SUGAR

TOP TIP
If pomegranate is too tart for your taste buds, substitute it with sweet passion fruit. As well as being the perfect tropical summer treat, it's packed with dietary fibre.

Hot chocolate

Satisfy your comfort-food cravings
with this healthy winter warmer

Serves: 2
Preparation time: 2 minutes
Cook time: 3-5 minutes

INGREDIENTS

3 tsp cocoa power
1 tbsp cold milk
200ml hemp milk
1 tsp blackstrap molasses
1 small ripe banana, chopped
Dark chocolate, to serve

METHOD

1 Add the cocoa powder to a jug and mix to a paste with milk.

2 Meanwhile, warm the hemp milk in a saucepan with the molasses and stir until dissolved. When hot (but not boiling), mix into the cocoa paste.

3 Add the banana and whizz in a blender, then return to the saucepan and heat for a minute.

4 Pour into a cup, grate a little dark chocolate on top and serve.

PER SERVING

161	5g	7g	1.5g	18g	1g	18g
CALORIES	PROTEIN	FAT	SAT FAT	CARBS	FIBRE	SUGAR

Contacts

HEALTH FOOD STORES

Alara
alarashop.com
0207 837 1172

Food For Living
foodforliving.co.uk
0132 227 8790

Goodness Direct
goodnessdirect.co.uk
0871 871 6611

Holland & Barrett
hollandandbarrett.com
0844 372 8926

Natural Grovery
naturalgrocery.co.uk
0208 749 1781

Planet Organic
planetorganic.com
0207 220 9060

Real Foods
realfoods.co.uk
0131 556 1772

The Nutri Centre
nutricentre.com
0208 752 8450

Whole Foods
wholefoodsmarket.com
0207 368 6100

FOOD DELIVERY SERVICES

Abel & Cole
abelandcole.co.uk
0845 262 6262

Daylesford Organic Farm
daylesford.com
0160 873 1700

Doves Farm
dovesfarm.co.uk
0148 868 4880

Farmaround Organic
farmaround.co.uk
0174 882 1116

Gousto
gousto.co.uk
0208 743 4187

Graig Farm Organic
graigfarm.co.uk
0168 662 7979

Jessica's Recipe Bag
jessicasrecipebag.co.uk
020 3609 8696

Organic Delivery Company
organicdeliverycompany.co.uk
0207 739 8181

Riverford Organic Farms
riverford.co.uk
0180 376 2059

DIET DELIVERY SERVICES

Balance Box
balancebox.com
0333 123 0818

Body Chef
bodychef.com
0800 783 7083

Diet Chef
dietchef.co.uk
0845 094 9796

My Food
myfood.co.uk
0120 269 7100

Nosh Detox
noshdetox.com
0845 257 6674

Pure Package
detoxkitchen.co.uk
0207 720 3250

Raw Fairies
rawfairies.com
0844 209 2303

Soulmate Food
soulmatefood.com
0870 803 3833

The Detox Kitchen
nealsyardremedies.com
0207 924 7548

HEALTHY INGREDIENTS

Alpro
alpro.com/uk
0800 018 8180

Biona Agave Nectar
biona.co.uk
0208 547 2775

Clearspring
clearspring.co.uk
0208 749 1781

Good 4 U
good4u.co.uk
00 353 7 198 0031

Good Hemp Food
goodwebsite.co.uk

Linwoods
linwoodshealthfoods.com
0283 756 8477

Meridian
meridianfoods.co.uk
0196 276 1860

Mornflake
mornflake.com
0127 021 3261

Nairns
nairns-oatcakes.com
0131 620 7000

Naturya
naturya.com
0164 722 1598

Nutiva
nutivauk.com

Pukka
pukkaherbs.com
0845 375 1744

Quinola Mothergrain
quinola.com
0208 144 9112

Rude Health
rudehealth.com
0207 731 3740

Sun & Seed
sunandseed.com
0207 267 7799

The Chia Co
thechiaco.com.au
0203 009 3022

The Food Doctor
thefooddoctor.com
020 7792 6701

The Groovy Food Company
groovyfood.co.uk

The Raw Chocoate Company
rawchocolatecompany.com
0127 349 3331

Tiana Coconut Oil
tiana-coconut.com
0208 427 1695

Viridian Nutrition
viridian-nutrition.com
0132 787 8050

KITCHEN GADGETS

Cuisinart
cuisinart.co.uk
0870 240 6902

Joseph Joseph
josephjoseph.com
020 7261 1800

Kenwood
kenwoodworld.com/uk
0239 239 2333

KitchenAid
kitchenaid.co.uk
0800 988 1266

Kuhn Rikon
co-uk.kuhnrikon.com
0190 245 8410

Lakeland
lakeland.co.uk
0153 948 8100

Le Creuset
lecreuset.co.uk
0800 373792

Magimix
magimix.fr
0844 573 8655

Philips
philips-shop.co.uk
0844 338 0489

Prestige
prestige.co.uk
0151 482 8282

ProCook
procoook.co.uk
0844 888 8380

Russell Hobbs
uk.russellhobbs.com
0845 658 9700

Sage
sageappliances.co.uk
0844 334 5110

Tefal
tefal.co.uk
0845 602 1454

Vitamix
vitamix.co.uk
0808 156 6633

SUPPLEMENTS

Biocare
biocare.co.uk
0121 433 3727

Desirable Body
desirablebody.co.uk
0845 459 6140

EQ8
eq8energy.com
0195 385 1411

Forza
forzasupplements.co.uk
0845 519 6010

Healthspan
healthspan.co.uk
0800 731 2377

Maxitone
maxitone.com
0144 241 8500

Nature's Best
naturesbest.co.uk
0189 255 2030

Purition
purition.co.uk
0845 222 0174

Reflex
reflex-nutrition.com
0127 330 3817

Revital
revital.co.uk
0870 366 5729

Solgar
solgar.co.uk
0144 289 0355

The Good Whey Company
thegoodwhey.com
0845 602 1217

SNACKS

9 Bar
9bar.com
0149 041 2297

Bear
bearnibbles.co.uk
02071830621

Bounce
bouncefoods.co.uk
845 838 2579

Cherry Good
cherrygood.com
020 7655 8249

Clif
clifbar.co.uk

Dole
dole.co.uk
0132 229 3355

Dr Karg
drkarg.co.uk

Eat Natural
eatnatural.co.uk
0178 747 9123

Graze
graze.com/uk

Kallo
kallofoods.com
0845 602 1519

Nak'd, Trek
naturalbalancefoods.co.uk
0845 862 5340

Proper Corn
propercorn.com

Pulsin'
pulsin.co.uk
0145 272 8900

Raw Health
rawhealth.co.uk

Zico Coconut Water
uk.zico.com

Enjoy healthy eating

Now you've reached the end of this nutrition and recipe guide, we hope you're feeling motivated and inspired to adopt a healthier way of eating. Whether you want to beat the bulge, maintain a slim figure or eat better for sports performance, you're now equipped with the knowledge you need to reach your goal. You should already be enjoying the benefits of a balanced diet – more energy, weight loss, reduced risk of cardiovascular disease, better digestive health and glowing skin – and your kitchen will soon be your favourite room in the house. Keep it up, and tuck in!

GET IN TOUCH

We'd love to hear from you! Share your diet tips and recipe ideas with the *Health & Fitness* team and readers online at facebook.com/HandFmagazine or on Twitter @HandFmagazine.